Contents

Each of these excerpts is taken from *Sport and Exercise Science,* written by Jennifer Stafford-Brown, Simon Rea and John Chance and reprinted with kind permission of Hodder Arnold, 338 Euston Road, London NW1 3BH.

BTEC NATIONAL STUDY GUIDE

Sport and Exercise Sciences

Compiled from

Sport and Exercise Science

By Jennifer Stafford-Brown, Simon Rea and John Chance

Edexcel Learning
80 The Strand
London
WC2R 0RL

Part of the Pearson group of companies throughout the world

This Edexcel Learning Edition first published 2005

Compiled from

Sport and Exercise Science
By Jennifer Stafford-Brown, Simon Rea and John Chance, published by Hodder Arnold
ISBN 0 340 87176 8

ISBN-13 978 1 84479 589 5
ISBN-10 1 84479 589 6

Printed and bound in Great Britain by Hobbs the Printers Limited, Totton, Hants

Preface

This Study Guide for the BTEC National in Sport and Exercise Sciences has been published to give you a flavour of the resources that are available to support your course.

A good textbook fulfils many roles. If you have forgotten something your tutor told you in class, you can look it up in the book. If there is something you are not quite sure about or don't quite understand, you can get to grips with it at your own pace and in your own time. If you are unfortunate to miss a class then you can probably read about the topic you missed in the textbook.

Texts also have activities and case studies for you to do so you can see how much you have understood. If you realise you need help, you can then go back to your tutor. Activities also give you the opportunity to practise the skills you will need for assessment.

And most texts will take you beyond their covers! They give you useful websites to explore, they will suggest journals and magazines that will widen your researches and they will have lists of other books to read if you want to explore an issue in greater depth. Make the most of all these leads to broaden your horizons. You will enjoy your course more and you are likely to get better grades.

This Study Guide covers only four of the units you may study for your BTEC National but we hope you will find it useful and will want to make further use of the book that is presented here.

THE SMART WAY TO ACHIEVE YOUR BTEC NATIONAL

We all know people who seem to do well almost effortlessly – at work, at college and even when they are just enjoying themselves. Some of them may be clever or talented but not all of them – so what is their secret? And how does this relate to your BTEC National course?

Every year thousands of students enrol on BTEC National courses. Most are successful and obtain the full qualification. A few do not - either because they don't complete the course or because they don't achieve all the units they need. In some cases students who are successful are still disappointed because they don't achieve the grades they wanted. This can have serious consequences if their offers of a university place are based on the achievement of specific final grades.

The difference between students who don't do as well as they had hoped, and those who do well, rarely has anything to do with brain power. After all, they were all accepted as suitable for the course in the first place. The difference is usually because some work efficiently and some do not. In fact, some students seem to go through college continually making life difficult for themselves – and then wonder why they have problems!

Students who work efficiently are **smart**. The strategies they use mean they are more likely to stay on the course (even if they have problems) and they regularly achieve better grades than other students.

So what do *you* need to do to be smart? First: read this guide. Second: follow it! Third: keep it safely and re-read it at regular intervals to refresh your memory.

The smart way to learn to be smart

In a nutshell

Working in a smart way means you are more likely to stay on your course, even if you have problems. You will also achieve better grades for doing the same amount of work!

Be smart about your course

There may be quite a gap between your interview at college and the date you start on your BTEC National course. In that time you will probably have forgotten a lot about what you were told. So the first thing to do is to refresh your memory and find out *exactly* what your course entails. You can do this by re-reading college information and also by logging onto the Edexcel website at www.edexcel.org.uk.

- There are three types of BTEC National qualifications and each has a different number of units.
  - The BTEC National Award has 6 units
  - The BTEC National Certificate has 12 units
  - The BTEC National Diploma has 18 units

  You should already know which type of BTEC National you are taking and how long your course lasts. It is useful to find out how many units you will study each term and how many units you will complete each year if you are on a two-year course.

- Every BTEC National qualification has a set number of **core units**. These are the compulsory units which every student must complete. There is also a range of **specialist units** from which you may be able to make a choice. These enable you to study particular areas in more depth. You need to check:
  - the title of each core unit and the topics it contains
  - the title of each specialist unit and the area it covers
  - whether you can choose any specialist units you want, or whether your choice is restricted. This may be because of the structure of the qualification or because your college does not offer the full range.

Knowing all about your course means that you are more likely to choose the most appropriate specialist units for your own needs and interests. You will be more mentally prepared and know what to expect. This also enables you to relate your everyday experiences to the topics you will be learning. You can then be alert to information that relates to your studies, whether you are watching television, reading an article, talking to your family or working – even in a part-time job a few hours a week. The more alert you are to these types of opportunities, the more you will benefit.

In a nutshell

Log on to www.edexcel.org.uk and check the exact content of your BTEC National course. Download the *Student's Guide* for your course which describes the course structure and the unit titles and check with your tutor which you will study each term. Check the course specification to find out the exact content of each unit and check the specialist units that are offered at your college before you select your specialist units. Always be alert to all sources of useful information that relate to your course.

Be smart about resources

A resource is anything that helps you to achieve your goal and so, generally speaking, the more you have the better! You will be introduced to many college resources during your induction, such as the library, the learning resource centre(s) and the computer network. However, most students never actually sit down and list all the resources they have. This is worthwhile because you will probably have far more than you realise. The easiest way is to divide up your resources into different categories and make a list under each heading.

There are two aspects to resources. Knowing what they are and using them properly! The main types of resources to consider are given below.

- **Course materials** These include this Student Guide, all the materials on the Edexcel website, all the information given to you during induction, the textbook(s) you use for particular units, the handouts you are given in class and the notes you make in class. They also include resources you are asked to provide yourself, such as lined paper, folders for storing notes, dividers for sub-dividing topics in your folders, pens, pencils, a hole punch, calculator and a good dictionary. These, by the way, are all essential resources – not optional extras you can scrounge from someone else!

  If you are smart then you always have the right resources for each lesson or session because you get organised in advance. You also file handouts and notes *promptly* in the right place in the right folder so that you can find them again quickly. You have clearly labelled dividers and your notes have a clear heading so that you can find information easily. If you are writing up your own notes from research then you will have made a clear note of the source of your information. How to do this is given in the IVA guide *Ten Steps to a Great IVA*.

- **Equipment and facilities** These include your college library and learning resource centre(s); the college computer network; other college equipment you can use, such as laptop computers and photocopiers; electronic information resources, such as Internet access, electronic journals and CDs; equipment you have at home – such as a computer; specialist equipment and facilities relevant to your particular course.

  Libraries can be baffling if you don't understand the system used to store books: your college computer network is of limited use if you don't know the difference between an Intranet and the Internet or realise that information is stored on CDs as well as in books. Library and resource centre staff are employed to give you help and advice if you need it – so don't hesitate to ask them! You also need to find the recommended way to transfer data between your home computer and college if your options are limited because of IT security. It is also very important that you check the regulations or guidelines on using the Internet and computers in your college so that you make the most of the equipment without falling foul of any of the rules that apply.

- **People** These include your tutor(s), specialist staff (such as library and resource centre staff), your employer and your colleagues at work, your relatives and friends who have particular skills or who work in the same area you are studying.

Smart students have their own resources

Most people will be keen to help you if you are courteous, well prepared and are not trying to get them to do the work for you! Prepare a list of open questions if you want to interview someone. These are questions that can't be answered with a 'yes' or 'no'. Work down your list but aim to get the person talking freely whilst you make notes. Unless they wander far from the topic you will find out more this way. Then do a final check that you have covered all the areas on your list and get a contact number in case you need to speak to them again. Don't forget to say thank you – and try not to overuse one particular person.

One word of warning! Be careful about asking for help from a friend who has already done the same course and *never* be tempted to borrow their assignments. Tutors can soon tell if the work isn't in your own personal style, or if it varies in style. In addition, assignments are normally changed each year and answers are expected to be up-to-date, so an answer from a previous year is unlikely to be of much use.

- **Your own skills and abilities** Obviously if you have excellent IT skills then you will produce your written assignments more easily. You will also be better at researching online if you know and understand how to use the Internet and have included useful sites in your Favourites list. Other vital skills include being able to recognise and extract key information from a book, being able to summarise and able to type up your work relatively quickly and accurately. As you will see as you work through this Guide being well-organised and using your time wisely are also invaluable skills and can make all the difference to your final grades.

  You can assess yourself as you read this Guide by listing those areas in which you are weak and need to improve your skills. Then talk to your tutor about the best way to do this.

In a nutshell

Resources are vital because they help you to succeed. If you list your resources you may find there are more than you think. Then you must use them wisely. This includes storing handouts safely and thanking people who help you. You also need to develop skills and abilities which will help you to work more easily – such as improving your Internet and typing skills.

Be smart about time

Some weeks you may find you have very little to do – so you can manage your workload easily. Then everything changes. In a short period of time you seem to be overwhelmed with work to do. If you are unlucky, this will coincide with a time when you also have family, personal or work commitments as well. So – how do you juggle everything and still stay in control?

There are several skills you need to be able to do this.

- **Record important dates in advance** Keep a homework diary or (even better) a wall chart and mark all key dates in colour. You can devise your own system but it is useful to enter assignment review dates with your tutor in one colour and final deadline dates in another. Keep your chart up-to-date by adding any new dates promptly every time you are given another task or assignment. This gives you prior warning when important dates are looming and, if nothing else, stops you from planning a heavy social week for the same time!
- **Prioritise your work** This means doing the most important and urgent task first. This is normally the task or assignment with the nearest deadline. The exception is when you have to allow for the availability of other people or other resources. For example, if you have two assignments to do and one involves interviewing three people, it is sensible to schedule the interviews first. If you need to send off for information it is also sensible to do this promptly, to allow plenty of time for it to arrive. It also means allowing enough time to print out your assignment well before the deadline – unless you are prepared to join the long queues of students who have the same deadline as you and who are all trying to print out their work at the last minute!
- **Plan your work** This means analysing each task and estimating how long it will take. For example, you may estimate that an assignment will take you one hour to plan, six hours to research, four hours to type up

Be smart about time

and one hour to check. In this case you need *at least* twelve hours to do the work. If you are sensible you will allow a little more, in case you encounter any problems or difficulties. It is wise to schedule fixed times to work and then plan to give yourself time off when you have completed a task or are 'between' tasks or assignments.

- **Regularly review your progress** You need to check regularly that you are on schedule. It is easy to spend much longer than you think on some tasks – either because you get bogged down or because you become too absorbed. This will mean you have to do the rest of the work in a rush and this may affect your grade.
- **Be smart – but be kind to yourself too!** If you are over-conscientious you may be tempted to burn the midnight oil to keep up-to-date. This isn't wise on a regular basis because no-one does their best work when they are over-tired. In this case remember to *target* your efforts where they will count most – rather than try to have everything perfect. Schedule in some breaks and relaxation time too; you are allowed a treat from time to time! If your problem is just the opposite – and you struggle to stay focused if you're not in the mood for work – then you need to practise a little more self-discipline. One trick is to find an aspect of a task that you will find easy or really enjoy. Then start with this to get yourself going. Aim to complete a fixed amount of work before you give yourself a small reward – such as a fifteen-minute break or a bar of chocolate!

You can find more detailed information on planning your work and reviewing your progress in the IVA Guide *Ten Steps to a Great IVA*.

We all need a treat from time to time

In a nutshell

Your workload may be unpredictable and some weeks will be worse than others. You will cope better if you note down all key dates in advance, prioritise properly, plan realistically the time work will take and regularly review your progress. Target your efforts so that you can take sensible breaks and start with tasks you enjoy to motivate yourself.

Be smart about assignments

Assignments are the main method of assessment on all BTEC National courses. Edexcel specifies the exact assessment criteria for each unit in a grid. In plain English, this is the list of skills and knowledge you must demonstrate to achieve a pass, merit or distinction. You will find these in your course specification immediately after the content of each unit.

There are two types of assignments.

- There are those that are **internally** set. In this case the assignments are set and marked by your own tutors. Each assignment will include tasks and activities that enable you to produce evidence directly linked to the assessment criteria for a particular unit. Most units have internally set and assessed assignments.
- Alternatively there are **externally set** assignments. In this case an **Integrated Vocational Assignment (IVA)** is set by Edexcel.

In both cases Edexcel checks that centres are assessing assignments correctly and that all centres have the same standards.

Many people panic at the thought of assignments, but being smart means you are well-prepared and won't break any golden rules!

- Always check the assessment criteria grid for the unit in advance, so that you know what to expect.
- The grid is divided into three main columns which state what you must do to achieve a pass, a merit and a distinction grade. The main word, which tells you what to do, is called a **command word.** You must understand the command word *and obey it* to obtain a specific grade. This is dealt with in more detail in the next section.
- Read the assignment brief *thoroughly* and query anything you do not understand with your tutor.
- Check those tasks which must be all your own work and which (if any) you will complete as a member of a group. If you are asked to do any work as a member of a team then you must always identify your own individual contribution to each task.

- *Always* remember that plagiarism (copying someone else's work) is an extremely serious offence and will result in disciplinary action. *Never* be tempted to share your work (or your disks or CDs) with anyone else and don't ask to borrow theirs!
- Check the other rules that apply. These will include
  - whether you can discuss your research or draft answers with your tutor – and when you must do this
  - the college-set deadline date for submission – and the penalties for handing in work late (this might mean your assignment not being assessed)
  - what to do if you are absent when the assignment is due or have a serious personal problem which affects your ability to complete the work on time. There is normally an official procedure for obtaining an extension. This is only when mitigating circumstances apply and can't be used just because you fail to plan properly!
- Make sure you answer every question fully and present your information according to the instructions. You may, for instance, have to provide information in a table or report rather than simply answering questions. You will get a lower grade if you ignore important presentation instructions.

In a nutshell

The assessment criteria grid for each unit states what you must provide evidence against to achieve a pass, merit or distinction grade. It is important that you read and understand this, as well as the assignment brief, and obey all the instructions. Check you know any other rules that apply, such as how to apply for an extension to the deadline if you have a serious personal problem. Then answer the questions fully and present the work as required.

Sadly, over-sleeping doesn't count as a serious personal problem

Be smart about command words

Command words are used to specify how a question must be answered, eg 'describe', 'explain' or 'analyse'. These words are often related to the level of answer required. You will therefore find these command words in the assessment grid and you will usually see, for example, that 'describe' will get you a pass grade. However, you would need to do more than give a straightforward description to get a merit or distinction grade.

Many students don't get the grades they should for an assignment because they do not realise the difference between these words. Instead of applying their knowledge (for a merit grade) they simply give a brief explanation or a list. Just listing *more* facts will not improve your grade; you must show you can use your knowledge.

The chart below shows you what is usually required when you see a particular command word. You can use this, and the answers below, to identify the difference between the types of answers required for each grade. Remember these are just *examples* of acceptable answers to help you. The exact response required will often depend upon the way a question is worded so check with your tutor if you are unsure what it is you have to do.

To obtain a pass grade you must prove your knowledge and understanding by giving the relevant facts clearly and concisely.

If it says:	This means you should:
Describe	Give a clear description that includes all the relevant features. You might want to think of this as 'painting a picture in words'.
Define	Clearly explain what a particular term means and give an example, if appropriate, to show what you mean.
Design*	Create a plan, proposal or outline to illustrate a straightforward concept or idea.
Explain how/why	Set out in detail the meaning of something, with reasons. This is more difficult than 'describing' or 'listing' so it can often help to give an example to show what you mean. Start by introducing the topic and then give the 'how' or 'why'.
Identify	Point out (ie choose the right one) or give a list of the main features.
Illustrate	Include examples or a diagram to show what you mean.
Interpret	Define or explain the meaning of something.
List	Provide the information in a list, rather than in continuous writing.
Outline	Write a clear description but not a detailed one.
Plan	Work out and explain how you would carry out a task or activity.
State	Write a clear and full account.
Summarise	Write down the main points or essential features.

Q Describe the Apple iPod.

Below is an example answer that would achieve a pass grade.

A The Apple iPod is a digital player on which music can be stored and played without the need for CDs or tapes. Music is stored on an iPod by transferring MP3 music files that have been downloaded from the Internet or copied from a CD. The Apple iPod with the largest capacity will store up to 10,000 songs and costs about £420. A mini version is much cheaper but stores far fewer – about 1,000 – for about £180. Both have been praised in reviews for their excellent sound quality, ease of use and stylish design.

* You may also find the word 'design' at merit level, as you will see below.

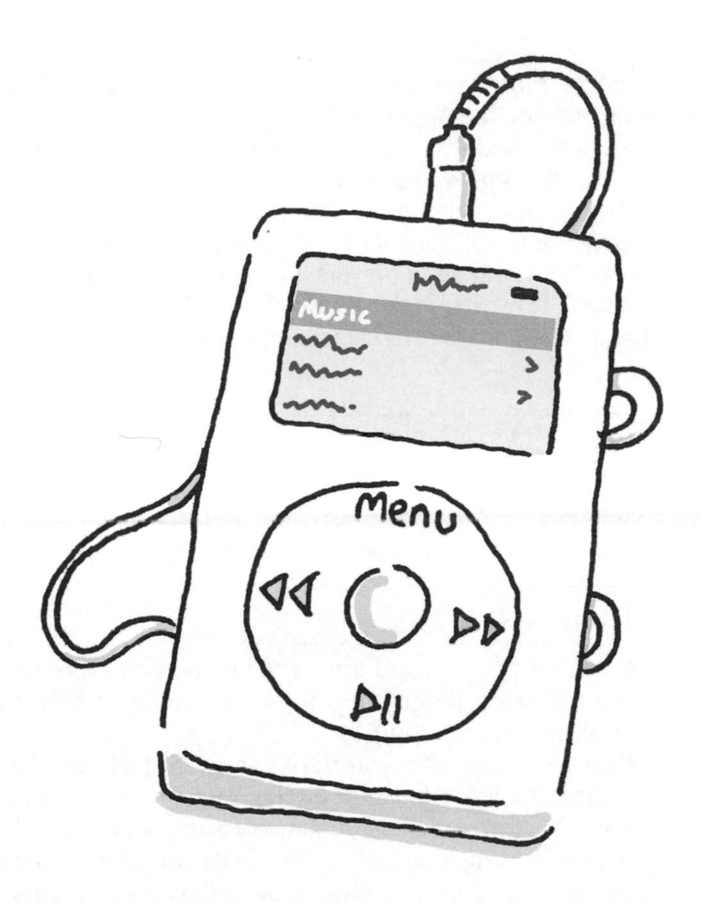

To obtain a merit grade you must prove you can apply your knowledge in a specific way.	
If it says:	This means you should:
Analyse	Identify separate factors, say how they are related and how each one contributes to the topic. This is one step up from the explanation you gave at pass level.
Compare/contrast	Identify the main factors that apply in two or more situations and explain the similarities and differences or advantages and disadvantages.
Demonstrate	Provide several relevant examples or related evidence which clearly support the arguments you are making. If you are doing a practical subject, this might be, e.g. showing your computer or coaching skills.
Design	Create a plan, proposal or outline to illustrate a relatively complex concept or idea.
Assess	Give careful consideration to all the factors or events that apply and identify which are the most important and relevant.
Explain in detail	Provide details and give reasons and/or evidence to clearly support the argument you are making.
how/why Justify	Give reasons or evidence to support your opinion or view to show how you arrived at these conclusions.

Q Analyse why Apple iPods are so popular.

Below is an example answer that would achieve a merit grade.

A Apple is one of several brands of MP3 players on the market. Rivals include the iAudio player and the Sony net walkman. Some rivals are cheaper than the iPod, so price is not the main reason for Apple iPod popularity. The iPod took off because its stylish design looked so good and there was some great advertising that turned it into the 'must have' item as early as Christmas 2003. It was also praised more by reviewers than other digital players. The Apple iPod stores music on a moving hard disk whereas some players store it on computer chips. Hard disk players have better sound quality and greater storage capacity. The Apple is also easy to use. Apple then developed the brand by adding accessories and introducing the mini iPod which comes in five different colours. Apple is also popular because it was the first to develop a portable MP3 player and supports its customers with its iTunes music store online. Downloads from the site aren't compatible with other players and so iPod users are tied to the iTunes site. Many people have criticised this. Apple, however, is the brand that is cool to own – so much so that over 10 million Apple iPods were sold in 2004 out of total sales worldwide of between 20 and 25 million portable music players.

To obtain a distinction grade you must prove you can make a reasoned judgement based on evidence.

If it says:	This means you should:
Appraise	Consider the plus and minus points and give a reasoned judgement
Assess	Must make a judgement on the importance of something. It is similar to 'evaluate' (see below).
Comment critically	Give your view after you have considered all the evidence. In particular decide the importance of all the relevant positive *and* negative aspects.
Criticise	Review a topic or issue objectively and weigh up both plus and minus points before making a decision. It is similar to 'comment critically'.
Draw conclusions	Use the evidence you have provided to reach a reasoned judgement.
Evaluate	Review the information and then bring it together to form a conclusion. Give evidence for each of your views or statements.
Evaluate critically	Decide the degree to which a statement is true or the importance or value of something by reviewing the information. Include precise and detailed information and assess possible alternatives, bearing in mind their strengths and weaknesses if they were applied instead.

Q Evaluate the effect of Apple iPods on the music industry.

An example answer that would achieve a distinction grade:

A Apple iPods – together with other digital music players – have helped to give the music industry a new lease of life. In the late 1990s music companies were alarmed that the Internet could ruin their business because of illegal file sharing and they forced the Napster website to close down. This site had allowed music fans to log on and exchange songs free of charge. Music companies also took legal action against private individuals. A famous case was of an American girl of 12 whose mother had to pay $2,000 in fines, which frightened other parents. However, the development of portable digital music players has boosted the popularity of legal download sites such as Apple iTunes, MyCokeMusic and the new Napster subscription service, which sell tracks for about 80p each. These enable music fans to select and store only the tracks they want to hear, rather than have to spend money on a CD album that may contain many tracks they don't want. In Britain in 2004, 5.7 million download tracks were sold compared with virtually none in 2003 and sales are predicted to double in 2005. This growth is being fuelled by global sales of portable music players – the most popular of which is the Apple iPod. The music industry is taking advantage of the trend by pre-releasing tracks online and there is now an official download chart. By 2009, experts predict that the digital market could be worth 25% of total music sales, compared to a mere 1.5% in late 2004. There is no doubt that the Apple iPod, and other portable digital music players, have been a major factor in this huge growth rate.

In a nutshell

The assessment criteria grid for each unit states what you must know to get a pass, merit or distinction grade. It is vital that you understand the command words used and obey them or you will not achieve the best grade possible.

Be smart about your grades

On the Edexcel website you can download a form called *Recording Your Achievement*. This enables you to record the grade for each unit you complete. The form also tells you how many points you achieve for gaining a Pass, Merit or Distinction for each unit and how these are added together to obtain your final grade(s). You obtain *one* final grade if you are taking a BTEC National Award, *two* final grades if you are taking a BTEC National Certificate and *three* final grades if you are taking a BTEC National Diploma.

This is very important information, because it helps you to plan where to target your efforts, particularly later in the course.

- Remember that you will obtain more overall points if you divide up your time so that you put the most effort and work into areas where you are weak, rather than spending the most time on assignments you enjoy or find easy! Although it is tempting to keep working on something you like doing, even when you have already done a good job, the danger is that you then don't do so well in other assignments that you have neglected or where you have cut corners. The secret is to put in the right amount of effort in *every* assignment to get the grade you need. For topics you find easy, this may mean you need to spend less time on the assignment than for work you find difficult – despite the fact that you may be tempted to do exactly the opposite! If you do consistently well in all your assignments you will find that this results in higher overall grades than if you do very well in some but poorly in others.
- Keeping your grade profile up-to-date and discussing it with your tutor at regular intervals is an excellent way of keeping yourself on track throughout the course.

In a nutshell

If you are smart you will plan to manage your grades and your overall profile. Do this by recording your grades, spending more time on important or difficult assessments and discussing your profile, as you go, with your tutor.

Be smart at work or on work experience

On some BTEC National courses there is a vocational element and you will need evidence from work or work experience to prove your skills and abilities. In this case your tutor will give you a logbook to keep. On other courses, workplace evidence is not essential but the knowledge and practical experience you gain is still extremely useful, if not invaluable. This only applies, of course, if you are smart enough to recognise the opportunities that occur. Relevant events are likely to include:

- your induction and any subsequent training courses you are asked to attend – even if these are only very short, work-based sessions
- any performance reviews or appraisals you have with your supervisor or boss
- your dealings with customers of the organisation – particularly if you had to respond to a difficult enquiry or solve a problem.

Your tutor will tell you how to get a witness statement

- the rules, regulations or guidelines that you must follow. You should think about why these have been put in place as well as the consequences of not abiding by them
- your own duties and specific areas of responsibility
- your relationships with your colleagues and how you resolve any problems or difficulties that occur
- skills you have learned or developed by being at work – from time keeping to achieving targets.

If you have to provide formal evidence then one method is to ask your manager, supervisor or colleagues for a **witness statement**. This is a formal document that confirms something you have done and when you did it. Your tutor will give you a form for this. It is also useful to keep your own work diary and to jot down important things that happen that you could use as evidence in current or future assignments to support your arguments for a merit or distinction grade question.

In a nutshell

Work experience may be an essential part of your BTEC National course. Even if it is not, you will gain many useful skills at work that can help you to achieve your award. Make a note of all key events and activities you are involved in. If you need formal evidence, ask your boss for a witness statement.

Be smart about key skills

Key skills are so-called because they are considered invaluable to everyone at work. Most BTEC National students study for a key skills award and in this case the majority of key skills will often be integrated into your main programme of study. This not only helps you to improve your skills, it also means you have the potential to achieve additional points when you submit your UCAS application. Unfortunately not all students complete their key skills awards and so fail to achieve their maximum points score. This is less likely to happen if you are smart and get key skills to work for you, and don't simply see them as more work to do!

- Always check the tracking sheet you are given with your assignments to see which key skills are covered by that particular piece of work.
- Take advantage of any specific classes for key skills, particularly Application of Number, unless you have passed a GCSE Maths examination that exempts you. Otherwise use the classes to improve your abilities.
- There are dozens of benefits if you can communicate effectively and there are almost endless opportunities for practice. You communicate every day – with your friends, family, tutor, boss and colleagues at work – in a variety of different ways. You spend time writing notes in class and writing up researched information. You prepare written documents for your assignments. You work with your classmates when you are doing role-plays or preparing a presentation. If you communicate effectively you will be able to make better presentations, ask the right questions when you are interviewing and write clearer answers to your assignments. You will then gain better grades for your BTEC National as well as your key skills award!
- Information technology is a crucial tool for completing work related tasks. If you develop your word processing skills and your Internet research skills you will produce better, more professional assignments more quickly and more easily. If you intend to continue studying you will find that good IT skills are invaluable at university. If you hope to start working in business when you leave your course then you can expect your future employer to take a keen interest in your IT abilities.

Make key skills work for you

- The 'wider' key skills are Improving own learning and performance, Working with others and Problem solving. These are likely to be required in many of your assignments. You will also demonstrate these skills if you go to work or are on work experience. Talk to your tutor about how you can use evidence from the workplace to help you to achieve your key skills award.

In a nutshell

There are many advantages to developing your key skills and achieving your key skills award. You will find this easier if you take advantage of all the opportunities you can to develop your key skills and use naturally occurring situations to provide much of the evidence.

Be smart if you have a problem

Many students have personal problems when they are studying. Knowing what to do in this situation makes all the difference. It also means you have one less thing to worry about when life is going wrong.

- Check your college induction information carefully. This should give you detailed information about the people you can talk to if you have a problem. Normally your personal tutor will be the first person on your list but there will be other people available, too, in case your tutor is absent or if you would prefer to talk to someone else in confidence.
- If you cannot find the information you want, ask a tutor you like and trust for advice – or visit the central student support area instead and ask there.
- All colleges have sets of procedures to cover different events. These include the following.
  - **The appeals procedure** This tells you what to do if you feel that an assignment has been unfairly marked. The obvious first step in this situation is to ask your tutor to explain the grade you have been given, and how this links with the assessment grid. Do this before you think of taking formal action. If you are unhappy with the tutor's explanation then talk to your personal tutor. If you are still unhappy then you have the right to make a formal appeal.
  - **Student complaint procedures** This is normally the 'last resort' for a student and is only used when a major worry or concern can't be resolved informally. You therefore have the right to make an official complaint but should only do so when you have exhausted all the other avenues open to you. It is not normally used for trivial matters.
  - **Student disciplinary procedures** This tells you what to expect if you are disciplined for any reason. Although it is wise to avoid trouble, if you do break a rule then it is sensible to read these procedures carefully. Always remember that an honest confession and an apology will normally count in your favour, so if you do have this type of problem, don't be tempted to make matters worse by being devious.
- All colleges will arrange confidential counselling for you if you have a serious personal problem. The counsellor is a trained expert, not a member of the teaching staff. Without giving away any personal details, your counsellor can ensure that you receive the additional support you need from the teaching team – such as more time for an assignment or time off for personal commitments.
- *Never* be tempted to keep a serious worry or problem to yourself. In this situation your concentration is affected, your time is more precious and allowance must be made for this. Being smart about the way you handle problems will enable you to stay on the course and means the problems will have far less impact on your final grades.

In a nutshell

All colleges have a wide range of support mechanisms and procedures in place that are invoked when problems occur. Take advantage of all the help you can get if you have serious personal difficulties. This can be used to support you on the course until the problem passes and your life is nearer to normal again.

SPORT AND EXERCISE PSYCHOLOGY

CHAPTER 3

Historically, sport science has focussed on how to improve the physical performances of sportspeople. Exercise physiology and biomechanics have developed a wealth of information in this area and it continues to include new, exciting research. New, improved training techniques have helped to push back the sporting barriers.

At the highest level, individuals will have similar physiological traits and fitness levels. Thus, they need to gain something extra to ensure that they will reach the very top, or win the gold medal rather than just reach the final.

Psychology (or study of (ology) the human mind (psyche)) can give athletes the mental edge over their rivals. Mental preparation by 'mental coaches' has become as crucial in modern sport as physical preparation. The recent work of John Syer in football, Stephen Bull with the England cricket team, Richard Cox with British bobsleigh teams and Dave Collins with British international weightlifters has shown the value of psychologically preparing athletes.

Many athletes and coaches will use psychological means to give their team an advantage or to minimise their disadvantage. In our own way we are all 'amateur' psychologists, as we discuss why we won or lost, and why people behave on the sports field in a certain manner. We rarely discuss the fitness or physical shape of players – usually we ask whether the team is motivated enough, or will be able to hold their nerve to win.

This chapter examines:

- the key factors of an individual's personality and motivation, and the effect these have on performance
- how the environments in which sport takes place will affect the performance of the team or individual
- the role of psychologists and the skills they use to influence performance.

PERSONALITY

Research in sport psychology has attempted to ask the following questions:

- Can sporting excellence be predicted by assessing personality?
- Are certain personality types attracted to certain sports?
- Does sport change a performer's personality?

From a non-scientific viewpoint the answer to all of these questions would appear to be 'yes'. However, before addressing these issues, we need to examine what is meant by the term 'personality', how personality can be tested and the different viewpoints psychologists take on personality and its development.

Credulous versus sceptical

Psychologists researching personality and its relationship to sporting performance fall into two categories: first, the credulous group, who believe that personality can be assessed and results can be used to make predictions about an individual's chances of success. Secondly, the sceptical group, who believe that personality research is limited in predicting the chances of sporting success.

Definitions

Personality

There are a range of definitions of **personality**, each with their merits and drawbacks. Kluckhorn and Murray (1949) say: '*each individual is like all other men, like some other men, like no other men*'.

This is a good starting point as it suggests we all have traits and behaviours that we share with other people, but we also have some particular to ourselves. However, it does lack depth of information; as does Cattell's (1965) attempt to define personality: '*that which tells what a man will do when placed in a given situation*'.

This suggests that if we know an individual's personality, we can predict behaviour. However, human beings tend to be less than predictable and can act out of character, depending upon the situation. Their behaviours may also be affected by their mood, fatigue or emotions.

Hans Eysenck (1960) sought to address these limitations with his definition:

> *the more or less stable and enduring organisation of an individual's character, temperament, intellect and physique which determines their unique adjustment to the environment.*

Eysenck's statement that personality is more or less stable allows the human element to enter the equation and explain the unpredictable. He also makes the important point that personality is 'unique'. We may have behaviours in common with other people, but, ultimately every person has a set of characteristics unique to themselves.

STUDENT ACTIVITY

Choose one of the following groups of sports people and discuss in pairs what personality characteristics each person has, based on your observations of their behaviours and interviews with them.

- Are there personality characteristics they have in common?
- Are these characteristics important in their sport?
- Can these characteristics explain their success?

Football
Roy Keane
Sol Campbell
Michael Owen
Rio Ferdinand
Ryan Giggs

Golf
Colin Montgomery
Tiger Woods
Sergio Garcia
David Duval
Darren Clarke

Athletics
Paula Radcliffe
Iwan Thomas
Denise Lewis
Ashia Hansen
Johnathon Edwards

Tennis
Andre Agassi
Tim Henman
Venus Williams
Pete Sampras
Martina Hingis

Rugby Union
Jason Robinson
Keith Wood
Martin Johnson
Robert Howley
Jonny Wilkinson

By giving labels to a person's character and behaviour in the activity, you have started to assess personality. By observing sports people we are using a **behavioural** approach, i.e. assessing what they are like by assessing their responses to various situations. In reality, our observations may be unreliable because we only see sports people in one environment, and although we see them interviewed as well, we do not know what they are truly like. A **cognitive** psychologist believes we need to understand an individual's thoughts and emotions as well as watching their behaviour. This we cannot do without the use of a questionnaire or an interview.

THEORIES OF PERSONALITY

Hollander's view of personality

Hollander addresses the issues discussed previously and shows how personality can only be understood by combining behaviourist and cognitive methods of assessment.

Hollander sees personality as being structured at three levels, as shown in Figure 3.1.

FIGURE 3.1 Hollander's personality levels

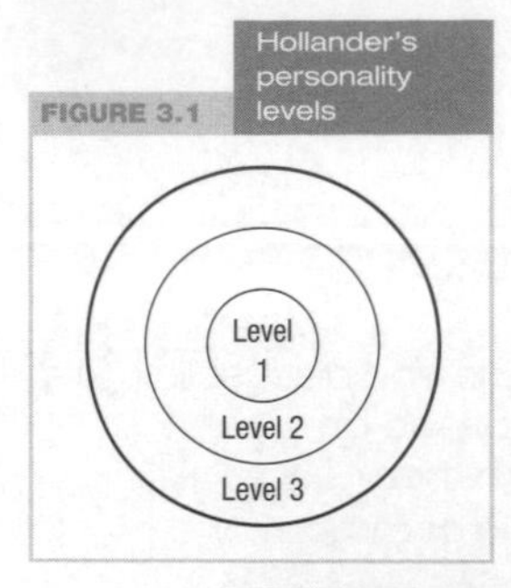

FIGURE 3.2 Endomorph body type

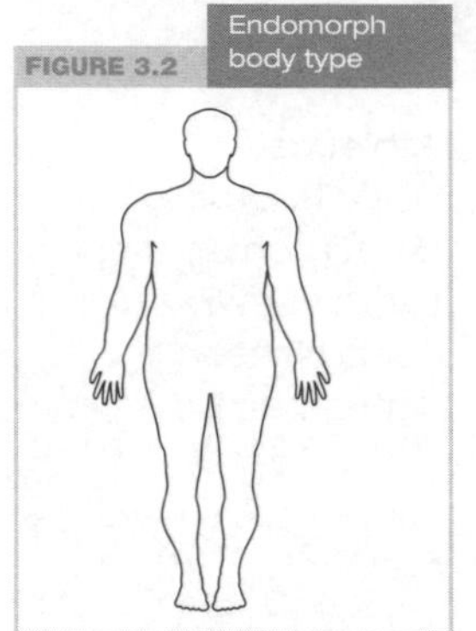

FIGURE 3.3 Mesomorph body type

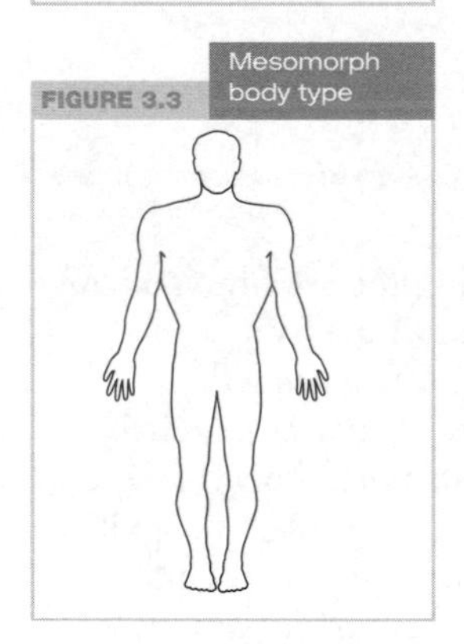

FIGURE 3.4 Ectomorph body type

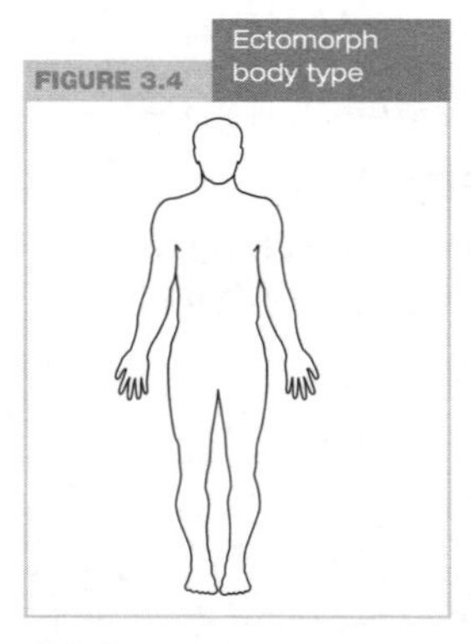

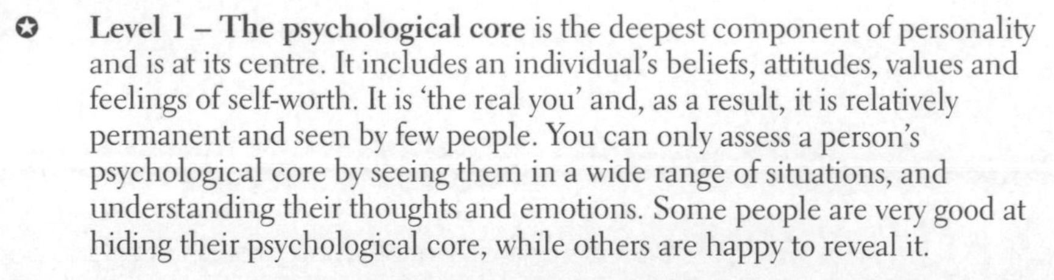

- **Level 1 – The psychological core** is the deepest component of personality and is at its centre. It includes an individual's beliefs, attitudes, values and feelings of self-worth. It is 'the real you' and, as a result, it is relatively permanent and seen by few people. You can only assess a person's psychological core by seeing them in a wide range of situations, and understanding their thoughts and emotions. Some people are very good at hiding their psychological core, while others are happy to reveal it.
- **Level 2 – Typical responses** are how we usually respond to situations and adapt to our environment. It is seen as the relatively consistent way we behave. If we have to describe our own or another's personality we would usually give labels to their typical responses. For example:
  - Tiger Woods – calm, laid back, even tempered
  - Roy Keane – aggressive, competitive, volatile
  - Paul Gascoigne – extroverted, happy-go-lucky, sociable.

  Our typical responses are good indicators of our psychological core, but, they can be affected by the social environment. A person who is very outgoing and sociable with his rugby-playing friends may become more reserved at a party with people he does not know.
- **Level 3 – Role related behaviours** are the shallowest level of our personality, and this level shows how we change our behaviours to adapt to the situation we are in. For example, throughout the day we may play the roles of sports person, student, employee, friend, son/daughter, coach, etc. In order to survive we need to adapt our personalities, as it would not be appropriate to behave on the sports field in the same manner as when studying in class. We need to modify our personalities to suit the situation. Some people play roles to hide their psychological core, while others are more open and let us see their true feelings. To illustrate this, observe the difference between Goran Ivanisevic's reaction to winning Wimbledon in 2001, compared with the more muted celebrations of Pete Sampras in recent years.

Sheldon's (1942) constitutional theory

One of the first attempts at a theory of personality was Sheldon's constitutional or body-type theory. He tried to relate personality to **somatotypes** (Figure 3.2–3.4 and Table 3.1).

Table 3.1 Body types and personality

Body type	Description	Personality type
Endomorph	Predominantly fat or pear shaped	Sociable, friendly, fun loving
Mesomorph	Predominantly muscular	Outgoing, confident, risk taking, adventure loving
Ectomorph	Predominantly lean or linear	Tense, shy, introverted, socially inhibited

This theory has gathered some 'folklore' validity in that we use first impressions to make assumptions about people's personalities. We use physique, clothing, hairstyles, piercing/tattoos and other visual information to assess what a person will be like and how they will behave.

In sport we see certain body types attracted to certain sports, and to be successful in these sports they need to exhibit certain behaviours, and thus we make generalisations about the personalities of these sports people.

For example, we have long-distance runners or cyclists who are predominantly ectomorphic, and we see them as being introverted and shy (traits needed because many hours of training are spent alone). We have rugby players and footballers who are predominantly mesomorphic and tend to be extroverted and group centred (traits needed in order to work together with team mates).

Even within a sport we can see individual differences. In track and field athletics the sprinters tend to be mesomorphs, and the middle to long-distance runners tend to be ectomorphs. It is easy to see personality differences between Maurice Green, Dennis Mitchell, Linford Christie and Haile Gabreselassie, Paula Radcliffe and Liz McColgan.

Physique may play a part in personality and behaviour, but people should not be **sterotyped**. It should not be assumed that people of certain statures will behave in certain ways, and physique cannot be used to assess success in sport. Above all it cannot be used to assess individual differences between people, and ignores the uniqueness of each person.

Trait theory

Trait or factor theory is based on the belief that personality is the sum of several traits that cause an individual to behave in a certain manner. Traits can be seen as being **enduring** and consistent behaviours across a range of situations. They could be compared to the 'typical behaviours' described in Hollander's theory. Trait theorists such as Cattell and Eysenck believed that traits could be assessed through the use of questionnaires, and these traits could then be used to predict how a person would behave in any given situation.

Eysenck's Personality Inventory (1965)

Hans Eysenck used the following questionnaire to assess personality through two dimensions: introversion/extroversion and stable/unstable. He called these 'types', and then showed the traits each type would exhibit.

These questions relate to how you behave, feel and act. Answer each one yes or no. The answer should reflect how you would usually act or feel, and they should be answered quickly to reflect your first reaction. Be sure to answer all questions.

	Question	Yes	No
1	Do you often long for excitement?		
2	Do you often need understanding friends to cheer you up?		
3	Do you stop and think things over before doing anything?		
4	If you say you will do something, do you always keep your promise, no matter how inconvenient it may be to do so?		
5	Do your moods go up and down?		
6	Would you do almost anything for a dare?		
7	Do you suddenly feel shy when you want to talk to an attractive stranger?		
8	Once in a while do you lose your temper and become angry?		
9	Generally, you prefer reading to meeting people?		
10	Are your feelings rather easily hurt?		
11	Do you occasionally have thoughts and ideas that you would not like other people to know about?		
12	Do you prefer to have a few but special friends?		
13	Do you daydream a lot?		
14	Are all your habits good and desirable ones?		
15	Can you usually let yourself go and enjoy yourself at a lively party?		
16	Would you call yourself tense or highly strung?		
17	Are you mostly quiet when you are with other people?		
18	Do you sometimes gossip?		
19	Do ideas run through your head so that you cannot sleep?		
20	Do you like the kind of work that you need to pay close attention to?		
21	Do you get attacks of shaking or trembling?		
22	Would you always declare everything at customs, even if you knew you would never be found out?		
23	Do you like doing things in which you have to act quickly?		
24	Do you worry about awful things that may happen?		
25	Have you ever been late for an appointment or work?		
26	Do you like talking to people so much that you never miss an opportunity of talking to a stranger?		
27	Are you troubled by aches or pains?		
28	Of all the people you know, are there some whom you definitely don't like?		
29	Would you say you were fairly self-confident?		
30	Are you easily hurt when people find fault with you or your work?		
31	Can you easily get some life into a dull party?		
32	Do you sometimes talk about things you know nothing about?		
33	Do you worry about your health?		

continues overleaf

048

continued

Scoring

1. E score

Question number	Response
1	Yes
3	No
6	Yes
9	No
12	No
15	Yes
17	No
20	No
23	Yes
26	Yes
29	Yes
31	Yes

For each answer you have that corresponds to the above responses give yourself one point. You will get a score out of 12 and this is your E score.

2. N score

Question number	Response
2	Yes
5	Yes
7	Yes
10	Yes
13	Yes
16	Yes
19	Yes
21	Yes
24	Yes
27	Yes
30	Yes
33	Yes

Again give yourself one mark for each answer you have that corresponds to the above responses. This will give you a score out of 12 for your N score.

FIGURE 3.5 Charting your score

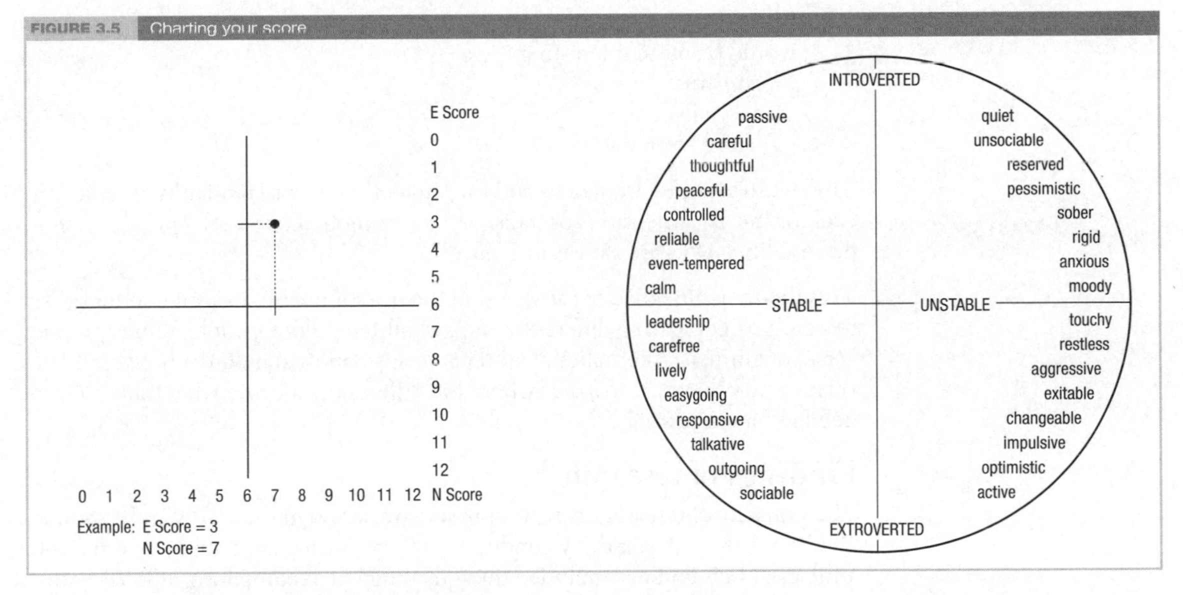

The E score describes to what extent you are introverted or extroverted; 1 being very introverted and 12 very extroverted.

The N score describes whether you are stable or unstable in your thoughts and emotions and the extent to which you worry about things. A score of 1 is very stable, while a score of 12 is very unstable or **neurotic**.

Research using Eysenck's Personality Inventory in sports

Morgan and Costill (1972) found that long-distance runners were mainly introverted, and Eysenck *et al.* (1982) found that extroverts were well represented in sports such as football, where the action is fast paced and gives them the excitement they need. They also found, that as a group, athletes are towards the unstable or neurotic end of the scale when compared with the general population. Perhaps this worry about performances gives them the stimulus to train hard and prepare properly.

Cattell's 16PF

Cattell's 16 Personality Factors test expanded on Eysenck's questionnaire to develop a test using 187 statements, such as:

3. I would rather have a house
   - **a.** in a sociable suburb
   - **b.** in between
   - **c.** alone in the deep woods

6. I hold back from criticising people and their ideas
   - **a.** yes
   - **b.** sometimes
   - **c.** no

11. It would be more interesting to be
   - **a.** a construction engineer
   - **b.** uncertain
   - **c.** a writer of plays

The questionnaires are scored and the subject is given a standardised score for each or the 16 dimensions or traits. These are plotted to reveal a profile. The personality factors are shown in Figure 3.6.

This theory is attractive because, using the questionnaire, we can conduct research by comparing different groups of athletes. For example, tennis players versus swimmers; international athletes versus county-standard athletes, athletes versus non-athletes, and assess where the differences are and what traits are needed for success.

Findings of research

The majority of research using trait theory was done in the 1970s and 1980s. In 1977 Schurr, Ashley and Joy conducted a large comparative study of over 2000 athletes. Their findings included the following when comparing athletes with non-athletes:

- athletes who played team sports were:
  - more outgoing and warm (A)
  - less intelligent (B)
  - more group dependent (Q2)
  - less emotionally stable and affected by feelings (C)

FIGURE 3.6 Cattell's 16 Personality Factors

FACTOR	Raw Score Form A	Raw Score Form B	Raw Score Total	Standard Score	LOW SCORE DESCRIPTION	STANDARD TEN SCORE (STEN) Average 1 2 3 4 5 6 7 8 9 10 (4.6 – 6.4)	HIGH SCORE DESCRIPTION
A					RESERVED, DETACHED, CRITICAL, ALOOF (Sizothymia)	• • • • •A• • • • •	OUTGOING, WARMHEARTED, EASY-GOING, PARTICIPATING (Affectothymia, formerly cyclothymia)
B					LESS INTELLIGENT, CONCRETE-THINKING (Lower scholastic mental capacity)	• • • • •B• • • • •	MORE INTELLIGENT, ABSTRACT-THINKING, BRIGHT (Higher scholastic mental capacity)
C					AFFECTED BY FEELINGS, EMOTION-ALLY LESS STABLE, EASILY UPSET (Lower ego strength)	• • • • •C• • • • •	EMOTIONALLY STABLE, FACES REALITY, CALM, MATURE (Higher ego strength)
E					HUMBLE, MILD, ACCOMMODATING, CONFORMING (Submissiveness)	• • • • •E• • • • •	ASSERTIVE, AGGRESSIVE, STUBBORN, COMPETITIVE (Dominance)
F					SOBER, PRUDENT, SERIOUS, TACITURN (Desurgency)	• • • • •F• • • • •	HAPPY-GO-LUCKY, IMPULSIVELY LIVELY, GAY, ENTHUSIASTIC (Surgency)
G					EXPEDIENT, DISREGARDS RULES, FEELS FEW OBLIGATIONS (Weaker superego strength)	• • • • •G• • • • •	CONSCIENTIOUS, PERSEVERING, STAID, MORALISTIC (Stronger superego strength)
H					SHY, RESTRAINED, TIMID, THREAT-SENSITIVE (Threctia)	• • • • •H• • • • •	VENTURESOME, SOCIALLY BOLD, UNINHIBITED, SPONTANEOUS (Parmia)
I					TOUGH-MINDED, SELF-RELIANT, REALISTIC, NO-NONSENSE (Harria)	• • • • •I• • • • •	TENDER-MINDED, CLINGING, OVER-PROTECTED, SENSITIVE (Premsia)
L					TRUSTING, ADAPTABLE, FREE OF JEALOUSY, EASY TO GET ALONG WITH (Alaxia)	• • • • •L• • • • •	SUSPICIOUS, SELF-OPINIONATED, HARD TO FOOL (Protension)
M					PRACTICAL, CAREFUL, CONVENTIONAL REGULATED BY EXTERNAL REALITIES, PROPER (Praxeeria)	• • • • •M• • • • •	IMAGINATIVE, WRAPPED UP IN INNER URGENCIES, CARELESS OF PRATICAL MATTERS, BOHEMIAN (Autia)
N					FORTHRIGHT, NATURAL, ARTLESS, UNPRETENTIOUS (Artlessness)	• • • • •N• • • • •	SHREWD, CALCULATING, WORDLY, PENETRATING (Shrewdness)
O					SELF-ASSURED, CONFIDENT, SERENE (Untroubled adequacy)	• • • • •O• • • • •	APPREHENSIVE, SELF-REPROACHING WORRYING, TROUBLED (Guilt proneness)
Q_1					CONSERVATIVE, RESPECTING ESTAB-LISHED IDEAS, TOLERANT OF TRAD-ITIONAL DIFFICULTIES (Conservatism)	• • • • •Q_1• • • • •	EXPERIMENTING, LIBERAL, ANALYTICAL, FREE-THINKING (Radicalism)
Q_2					GROUP-DEPENDANT, A 'JOINER' AND SOUND FOLLOWER (Group adherence)	• • • • •Q_2• • • • •	SELF-SUFFICIENT, PREFERS OWN DECISIONS, RESOURCEFUL (Self-sufficiency)
Q_3					UNDISCIPLINED SELF-CONFLICT, FOLLOWS OWN URGES, CARELESS OF PROTOCOL (Low integration)	• • • • •Q_3• • • • •	CONTROLLED, SOCIALLY PRECISE, FOLLOWING SELF-IMAGE (High self-concept control)
Q_4					RELAXED, TRANQUIL, UNFRUSTRATED (Low ergic tension)	• • • • •Q_4• • • • •	TENSE, FRUSTRATED, DRIVEN, OVERWROUGHT (High ergic tension)

A sten of	1	2	3	4	5	6	7	8	9	10	*is obtained*
by about	2.3%	4.4%	9.2%	15.0%	19.1%	19.1%	15.0%	9.2%	4.4%	2.3%	*of adults*

- athletes who played individual sports were:
  - more group dependent (Q2)
  - less anxious (Q4)
  - less intelligent (B)

Williams (1980) compared female athletes with female non-athletes and found that the athletes were:

- more independent (Q2)
- more aggressive and dominant (E)
- more emotionally stable (C)

The research proved fairly inconclusive and the theory is seen to have several flaws.

- The answers given to the questionnaire are influenced by mood and motivation.
- The situation and how it affects personality is not taken into account.
- Human beings are, by nature, unpredictable in their responses and their personalities cannot be labelled.
- Personality will change and develop over time.
- Trait approach may explain why people choose certain sports, but not how successful they will be.

Social learning theory

Social learning theory, or the situational approach, takes the view that personality is determined by the environment and the experiences a person has as they grow up. Other theories (e.g. trait) take the nature or biological approach to personality in that they see it as being largely genetic or inherited; the social learning theory sees personality as the result of nurture or upbringing.

Richard Cox (1985) outlines the two mechanisms of learning: modelling and social reinforcement.

1. **Modelling** – We observe and imitate the behaviour of significant others in our lives. At first, this is our parents and siblings, then our friends, teachers, sports stars and anyone we regard as a role model. We often hear sports people, such as Michael Owen and David Beckham, being praised for being good role models to young people; this means their conduct is good to observe and imitate.
2. **Social reinforcement** – This means that when a behaviour is rewarded positively it is more likely that it will be repeated; conversely, a behaviour negatively rewarded is less likely to be repeated. At an early age our parents teach us right and wrong by positively or negatively rewarding behaviour.

In sport there is a system of negative reinforcement to discourage negative behaviours on the sports field. Thus, rugby players get sent to the sin bin, cricketers get fined part of their match fee and footballers get yellow and red cards as a means of social reinforcement.

Young people will copy the behaviour of sports stars, as can be seen by the imitation of David Beckham and Freddie Ljungberg's haircuts. Another good example is in the England versus Mexico game of 1994, when the Mexican goalkeeper, Rene Higuitta, produced a scorpion kick to save a goal, and immediately young goalkeepers started to imitate. Eventually, the Football Association banned the move because they felt it was dangerous.

The situational approach is difficult to use to predict behaviour and analyse why some people are more successful than others. However, it can help us understand why people behave in certain ways, such as aggressively, due to past experiences and observations.

The interactional approach

The interactional approach considers the person's psychological traits and the situation they are in as equal predictors of behaviour.

behaviour = f (personality, environment)

Thus, we can understand an individual's behaviour by assessing their personality traits and the specific situation they find themselves in. Bowers (1973) says the interaction between a person and their situation could give us twice as much information as traits or the situational approach alone.

An interactional psychologist would use a trait–state approach to assess an individual's personality traits and then assess how these traits affect their behaviour in a situation (state). For example, an athlete who exhibited high anxiety levels as a personality trait would then have an exaggerated response to a specific situation.

Other personality measurements

Profile of mood states (POMS)

FIGURE 3.7 The positive mental health model

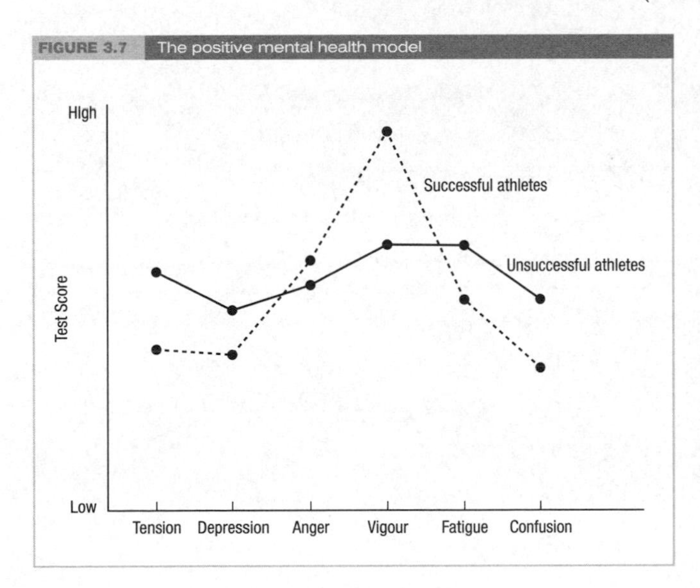

POMS was developed by McNair, Lorr and Droppelmann (1971) to show how moods changed in certain situations. The mood states assessed were tension, depression, anger, vigour, fatigue, confusion

Morgan's (1979) research using POMS developed the positive mental health model to predict athletic performance and success. He showed that if an athlete can exhibit the trait of vigour above population norms and all other traits below the population norm then their chances of success are greatly enhanced. He called this the 'Iceberg profile' as plotted in Figure 3.7. The figure also shows the profiles of less successful athletes.

Type A and type B personalities

This questionnaire was initially developed to identify people who were prone to stress and stress-related illnesses. However, it has some application to sport and exercise. The following questionnaire can be used to identify which personality type you fit into.

	Statement	Score	Statement
1	Don't mind leaving things temporarily unfinished	1 2 3 4 5 6 7	Must get things finished once started
2	Calm and unhurried about appointments	1 2 3 4 5 6 7	Never late for appointments
3	Not competitive	1 2 3 4 5 6 7	Highly competitive
4	Listen well, let others finish speaking first	1 2 3 4 5 6 7	Anticipate others in conversation by interrupting
5	Never in a hurry even when pressured	1 2 3 4 5 6 7	Always in a hurry
6	Able to wait calmly	1 2 3 4 5 6 7	Uneasy when waiting
7	Easy going	1 2 3 4 5 6 7	Always going at full speed
8	Take one thing at a time	1 2 3 4 5 6 7	Try to do more than one thing at a time
9	Slow and deliberate in speech	1 2 3 4 5 6 7	Vigorous and forceful in speech, using gestures
10	Concerned with satisfying self, not others	1 2 3 4 5 6 7	Want recognition from others for a job well done
11	Slow at doing things	1 2 3 4 5 6 7	Fast at doing things
12	Relaxed	1 2 3 4 5 6 7	Hard driving
13	Express feelings openly	1 2 3 4 5 6 7	Hold feelings in
14	Have a large number of interests	1 2 3 4 5 6 7	Have few interests
15	Satisfied with life	1 2 3 4 5 6 7	Ambitious
16	Never set own deadlines	1 2 3 4 5 6 7	Always set own deadlines
17	Feel limited responsibility	1 2 3 4 5 6 7	Always feel responsible
18	Never judge things in terms of quantity, just quality	1 2 3 4 5 6 7	Quantity is more important than quality
19	Casual about work	1 2 3 4 5 6 7	Take work very seriously
20	Not very precise	1 2 3 4 5 6 7	Very precise and careful about detail

Total your score ______

What does your score mean?

Between 0 and 29: a type B personality; you are usually relaxed and cope well with stressful situations.

Between 30 and 59: a type B personality; you are generally relaxed and cope adequately with stress.

Between 60 and 79: you have a mixed personality and show traits of both types. You should be aware when you exhibit type A behaviours.

Between 80 and 109: a type A personality; you do not cope well with stress and may be prone to stress-related illnesses.

Between 110 and 140: a type A personality; you are in a high-risk group, especially if you exhibit other factors which may contribute to heart disease.

Type A behaviour:

- highly competitive
- achievement oriented
- eat fast, walk fast, talk fast
- aggressive, restless and impatient
- find it difficult to delegate or not be in control
- experience high levels of stress

Type B behaviour:

- less competitive
- more relaxed
- delegate work easily
- take time to complete their tasks
- calm, laid back and patient
- experience low levels of stress

Type B's will exhibit the opposite types of behaviour to type As.

In sport we see both personality types being equally successful. However, with people exercising recreationally, we see higher levels of retention on their exercise programmes. Type As would benefit from exercise as it promotes type B-related behaviours.

ISSUES IN PERSONALITY TESTING

There are problems with personality testing, as can be seen by the difficulty in defining personality. We have no universally agreed definition of personality, so if we cannot decide what it is, how can we test it? This brings into question the **validity** of personality testing, i.e. are we testing what we say we are testing?

Secondly, we have covered five theories of personality and there are many more; so if we cannot decide which theory is correct, again we will struggle to understand and test it.

The way that people answer questions or may modify behaviour can create problems for the researcher. We all want to be seen in the best light, so may be untruthful in some of our responses to make ourselves look good. The way we answer questions will also depend upon our mood. For example, we will give different responses to a post-match questionnaire based on how we performed and the result! This brings into question the **reliability** of the testing.

Thirdly, there are ethical issues regarding testing, as results could be misused and a coach could use the results as a basis for his team selection. If he can predict how people will respond to a stressful situation, then he can use this to choose his team.

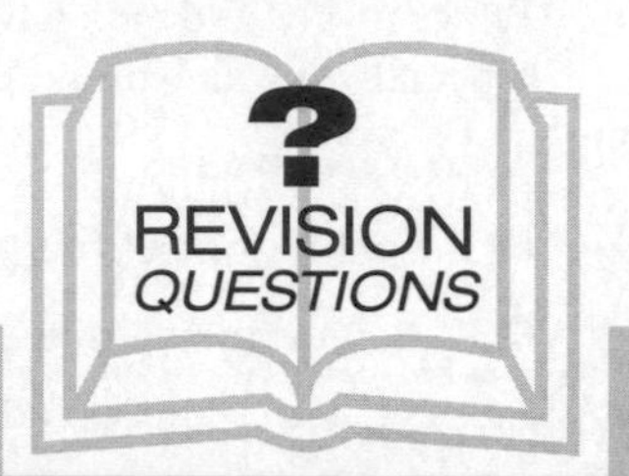

1) Choose one definition of personality and discuss its good points and bad points.
2) Discuss the three levels of personality as outlined by Hollander.
3) How does Sheldon (1942) see physique as influencing personality?
4) Explain the trait theorists' view of personality.
5) Outline the two ways that social learning theorists say we learn our behaviours.
6) What other factor does the interactional approach take into account that trait theory does not, and why is this important?
7) Explain what is meant by the 'iceberg profile'.
8) How do type A and type B personality types differ?
9) Discuss three problems regarding personality research in sport.

STRESS, AROUSAL AND ANXIETY

Stress is usually talked about in negative terms. People complain that they have too much stress or are stressed out; sports people claim the stress of competition is too much for them. However, we should not see stress as an entirely negative thing because it provides us with mental and physical energy to motivate us into doing things and doing them well.

If we did not have any stress in our lives, we might not bother to do anything all day. We need stressors to give us the energy and direction – without any stress we would become bored and psychologically stale. This type of positive stress is called **eustress** (good stress), however, if we have too much stress is can become damaging and we call this **distress** (bad stress).

eustress ________________________________ distress

Think of a recent competition that you very much wanted to win. Try to recall how you felt before this competition started.

The feelings you had are the symptoms of stress, and they can be separated into physical (the effects on your body), mental (the effect on your brain) and behavioural (how your behaviour changed).

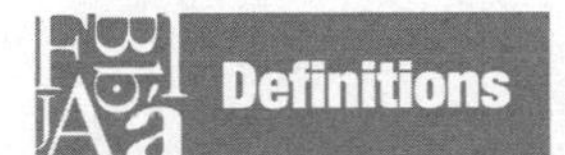

Stress
'*...any influence which disturbs the natural equilibrium of the body*' (Wingate, 1982).

Make a list of things which cause you stress. These may be related to the sports you play or other things in general life.

Too much stress in our lives over a long period of time can seriously damage our health, causing things like coronary heart disease, high blood pressure, ulcers, impotence, substance addiction, mental health problems and suicidal tendencies.

Sport is a source of stress for some sports people. As the importance of a game rises and the rewards for winning increase, so the symptoms of stress start to appear. The effect of this stress can be mixed, as sometimes it will bring out best performances and sometimes worst.

The classic definition of stress sees the body as having a natural equilibrium or balance, when the heart rate is at its resting level, the breathing rate at its resting level, and blood pressure at normal levels. Anything that changes these natural levels is a stressor. Theoretically, we could say we become stressed as soon as we get out of bed, as our heart rate, breathing rate and blood pressure all rise. Indeed, to some people the alarm going off is a real source of stress!

However, our bodies can cope with the stresses that it is subjected to on a daily basis and remain unaffected. We can compare it with the chair that you sit on everyday: as you put your weight on the chair it becomes stressed, but it is designed to deal with this stress and can cope for about twenty years without any problems. If you were to go away for a while and double your body weight, then sit on the chair, it may well break because it is not able to take the stress you have put upon it. Our bodies are similar to this: they can cope with normal levels of stress, but if too much stress is placed on us, or stress is put on us over a long period of time, then our bodies will start to suffer physical and mental breakdown.

Causes of stress

Chinese proverb:

> *That the birds of stress and worry fly above your head, this you cannot change; but that they build nests in your hair, this you can prevent.*

The causes of stress are many and varied, but crucially they are specific to an individual. For example, you can have two people in the same event, each with a different stress response.

The sources of stress can generally be divided into four categories.

1. **Internal** – Things we think about such as past memories and experiences, past injuries, our own feelings of self worth, and so on.
2. **External** – Things in our surroundings and our environment, such as competition, our opponents, the weather, spiders and snakes, transport problems.
3. **Personal factors** – People we share our lives with such as friends, family, partners; and life factors such as money and health.
4. **Occupational factors** – The job we do, the people we work with (the boss) and our working conditions. In sport it could include our relationships with team mates and coaches/managers.

Stress levels also depend upon personality. Those people who have a predominantly type A personality will find more situations stressful, as will people who have a high N score using Eysenck's personality inventory.

The physiology of stress

When we perceive ourselves to be in a situation which is dangerous, our stress response is activated. This has been developed as a means of ensuring our survival by making us respond to danger. For example, if we walking home at night through dark woods and we hear noises behind us our body will instigate physiological changes, called the 'fight or flight' response, as the body is preparing to turn and fight the danger or run away as fast as it can.

The response varies depending upon how serious we perceive the threat to be. The changes take place in our involuntary nervous system which consists of two major branches:

- the sympathetic nervous system
- the parasympathetic nervous system.

The **sympathetic nervous system** produces the stress response, and its aim is to provide the body with as much energy as it can to confront the threat or run away from it. The circulatory system also takes blood away from less important areas, such as the skin and stomach, and diverts it to the working muscles to provide more oxygen. The sympathetic system produces the following effects:

- increased adrenaline production
- increase in heart rate
- increase in breathing rate
- increased metabolism
- increased heat production
- muscle tension
- dry mouth
- dilated pupils
- hairs on the skin stand on end (to make us look bigger)
- digestive system slows down.

The **parasympathetic nervous system** produces the relaxation response, its aim being to conserve energy. It is activated once the stress has passed. The parasympathetic system produces the following responses:

- slowed heart rate
- slower breathing rate
- smaller pupils
- dry skin

- muscle relaxation
- slower metabolism
- lower body temperature
- saliva produced
- digestion speeded up.

It is not healthy for the body to be in a constant state of stress because of the activation of the sympathetic nervous system. The excess production of adrenaline is dangerous because the body requires more cholesterol to synthesise adrenaline. This excess cholesterol production raises blood cholesterol levels and is a risk factor for coronary heart disease (CHD).

Arousal and anxiety

Arousal and anxiety are terms related to stress. **Arousal** is seen as being a **positive** aspect of stress and shows how motivated we are by a situation. The more aroused we are, the more interested and excited we are by a situation. We can see this when we watch a football match involving a team we support: we are so aroused that we are engrossed in the action to the point of where we don't hear noises around us and time seems to go very quickly. During a match that does not arouse us to the same extent, we find that our attention drifts in and out as we are distracted by things happening around us.

Anxiety can be seen as a **negative** aspect of stress, and it may accompany high levels of arousal. It is not pleasant to be anxious and is characterised by feelings of nervousness and worry. Again, the stress and anxiety responses are unique to each individual.

Arousal and performance

Arousal levels will have an influence on performance, but it is not always clear-cut what this relationship is. The following theories help to explain the relationship.

Drive theory

This theory, initially the work of Hull (1943), states that as arousal levels rise, so do performance levels. This happens in linear fashion and can be described as a straight line (see Figure 3.8).

FIGURE 3.8 Drive theory

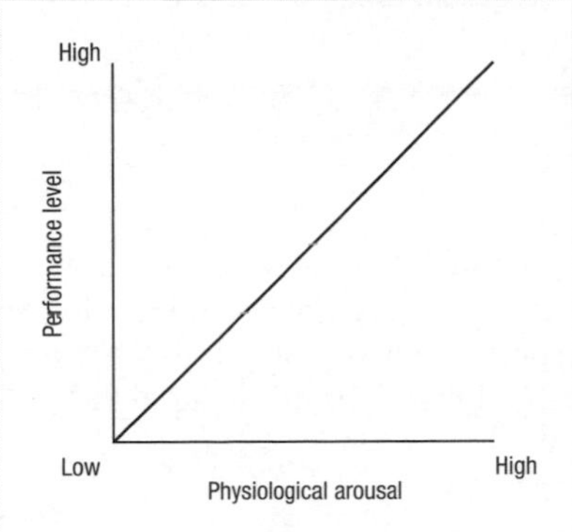

The actual performance also depends on the arousal level and the skill level of the performer. Arousal will exaggerate the individual's dominant response, meaning that if they have learnt the skill well their dominant response will be exaggerated positively, but if they are a novice, their skill level will drop to produce a worse performance.

This theory is too simplistic as it does not take into account the type of task performed. It might work for a strength-related task such as weight lifting or performing press ups, but for more complex tasks, such as playing snooker or throwing darts, it may not apply as the arousal levels may damage performance.

FIGURE 3.9 The inverted U hypothesis

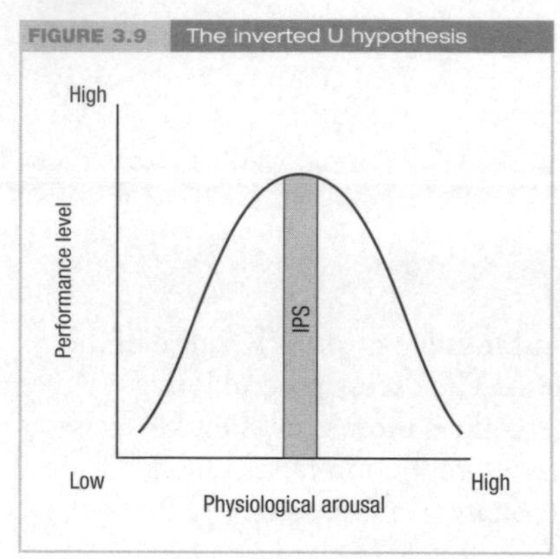

FIGURE 3.10 Catastrophe theory

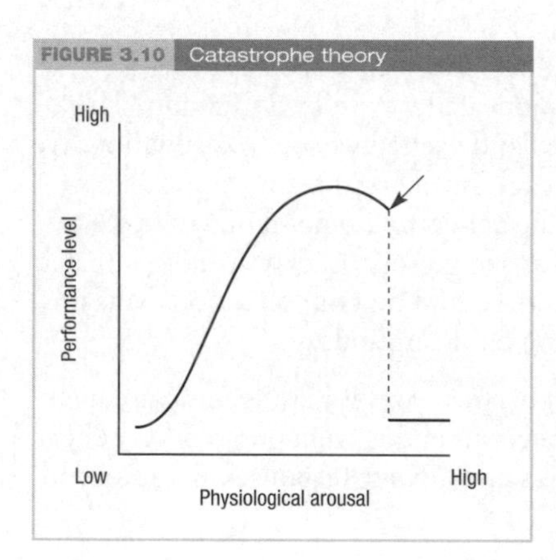

The inverted U hypothesis

This theory is based on the Yerkes and Dodson Law (1908) and seeks to address some of the criticisms of the Drive Theory. This theory agrees that arousal does improve performance, but only up to a point, and once arousal goes beyond this point performance starts to decline. Figure 3.9 shows the curve looking like an upside down U.

This theory's main point is that there is an optimum level of arousal before performance starts to diminish. This is also called the ideal performing state (IPS) and is often referred to as 'the Zone'. At this point the arousal level meets the demands of the task, and everything feels good and is going well.

This theory has been taken a step further by Hardy and Fazey (1988), who agree with the inverted U hypothesis, but say that once arousal level has passed, the IPS will drop off drastically, rather than in steadily (see Figure 3.10). The point where performance drops is called the point of catastrophe. The Americans refer to this phenomenon, when performance drops, as 'choking', and the history of sport is littered with examples of when people or teams have thrown away seemingly unassailable positions.

A classic example was in the British Open Golf Championships of 1999, when Jean van der Velde went to the 72nd hole of the tournament with a three-shot lead. All he had to do was hit the ball straight on to the fairway and then he would have five shots to get the ball down. However, Jean went for glory and sliced his drive into the rough, then chipped into the brook and had to take his shoes off to play the next shot. He eventually got down for a seven, which lead to a three-way play off and this he lost to Paul Lawrie.

Whole teams have also been known to choke collectively, such as the Brazilian football team in the World Cup final of 1998, when they were clear favourites but failed to perform in the final, losing 3–0 to France.

The effect of stress on performance depends upon a range of factors:

- personality of performer
- skill level of performer
- type of skill performed.

Oxendine (1970) focused on the skill level of sport when he developed his taxonomy of sport (Table 3.2). He showed that high levels of arousal would improve the performance of gross skills in sports, such as weight lifting; however, they would inhibit the performance of fine skills involving high levels of co-ordinated movement, such as golf or cricket.

Table 3.2 Oxeninde's taxonomy of sport

Arousal level	Sports
5	weight lifting; gym exercises; tackling in rugby; 200/400 metre racing
4	wrestling/judo; long jump; shot putt; long-distance running
3	soccer; basketball; high jump; gymnastics; boxing
2	tennis; baseball; fencing; diving
1	golf; archery; bowling; snooker; darts

Stress management

One of the key roles of the sport psychologist is to help performers to try to control their stress levels and maintain a level of arousal appropriate to the task they are performing. This is not an easy role as the individual personalities have to be taken into account, as do the differing skills of the sport. For example, a hooker in rugby is required to perform some gross skills, such as pushing in the scrum, tackling, rucking and carrying the ball forward; however, they then have to perform the fine skill of throwing the ball into the lineout, which requires low levels of arousal. A footballer also performs gross skills of tackling and blocking, then fine skills of passing, shooting and dribbling. In order to do this, the performers need to recognise when they have low and high levels of arousal, and when each is appropriate.

The aim of the sport psychologist is to get their athletes to be familiar with their optimum level of arousal, and then to teach them how to achieve and sustain that level of arousal.

The main methods of stress management are:

- progressive muscular relaxation
- mind-to-muscle relaxation
- biofeedback
- meditation/centering
- systematic desensitisation.

Progressive muscular relaxation (PMR)

This technique involves an athlete tensing and relaxing their muscle groups individually and sequentially in order to relax their whole body and their mind. It is also called muscle-to-mind relaxation, as muscles are tensed and relaxed in order to induce complete relaxation.

Each muscle is tensed and relaxed in order to teach the athlete the difference between a tense muscle and a relaxed muscle. After a muscle is tensed, the relaxation effect is deepened, which also has an effect on the involuntary muscles. The technique is practised using a series of taped instructions, or with the psychologist giving the instructions, and usually starts at the hands by making a tight fist and then relaxing. The tensing and relaxing carries on up the arms into the shoulders, the face and neck, then down to the stomach and through the hips and legs.

An example of an PMR training session follows:

> *Make a tight fist with both hands and hold for five seconds, feeling the tension in the hand and the forearm. Now relax and, as the muscles relax, feel the tension replaced by relaxation spreading through the muscle groups. Remember this sensation and feel how pleasant it can be. Now shrug your shoulders and feel the tension in your shoulders. Hold for five seconds, then relax and feel the relaxation spreading through your shoulders.*

These sessions last between 20 and 30 minutes, but they need to be practised about five times to gain the maximum effect. Each time they are practised they have an increased effect and an athlete can relax more quickly and more deeply, the aim being that when they need to use the relaxation technique quickly they can induce relaxation using a trigger, such as tensing the hand or the shoulders.

Mind-to-muscle relaxation

This technique is also called imagery and involves the use of a mental room or a mental place. This is a place where an athlete can quickly picture themselves in order to produce feelings of relaxation when they need to relax.

Again, it involves the athlete using a taped script or a psychologist giving instructions. Usually the psychologist asks an athlete to build a mental picture of a room; this is a room where they can feel relaxed and where there is somewhere to sit or lie down; it should be decorated in a pleasing manner. Alternatively, an athlete may imagine a relaxing place, such as somewhere they went on their holidays or a beach or quiet place where they feel calm and relaxed. The athlete is taught to vividly imagine this place and feel the sensations associated with being there. They do this about five times, so that eventually they can go there when they need to and are able to relax more quickly and deeply.

As the athlete relaxes their mind, they feel the sensations transferring to their muscle groups and they can achieve overall body relaxation. It tends to work best for individuals who have good skills of imagery; other individuals may feel that PMR is more effective for them.

Biofeedback

This method relies upon us being aware of what happens to our bodies when we become aroused and anxious. For example, we will experience changes in our heart rate, skin temperature and blood pressure. These can be monitored by various devices such as heart rate monitors and blood pressure monitors, or a biodot which monitors our skin temperature. As we learn to relax we will see falls in skin temperature and heart rate. The athlete starts to learn what relaxation feels like and can attempt to reproduce this feeling when they need it.

Centring/meditation

These techniques involve the athlete focusing on one thing, such as their breathing (centring) or a mantra (meditation), and by focusing their attention they become more and more relaxed. Again, these feelings of relaxation can eventually be produced when needed.

Systematic desensitisation

This technique was initially developed by psychologists to deal with people who had developed phobias. It involves a person being put in situations of increasing stress to slowly desensitise them to whatever they fear. For example, if a person had a fear of snakes they may take the following steps.

1. The person is shown a snakeskin.
2. The person is shown a picture of the snake.
3. The person is put in a room with the snake, but they cannot see it.
4. The person is put in the room with the snake in a glass cage.
5. The person is shown the snake by someone holding it.
6. The person attempts to touch the snake.
7. The person is able finally to hold the snake.

This technique can be applied to sport where athletes find themselves going into a situation more stressful than they are used to. The coach will seek to desensitise them by putting them in situations which simulate the stress and allow them to get used to it. For example, non-league football teams have used taped crowd noise during training sessions to prepare their players for the noise of a Premiership crowd; or they visit their opponent's ground before the match to get them used to the situation and limit their stress levels.

Cognitive control strategies

Cognitive control strategies are used to prepare an individual for their forthcoming performance and aspects within their performance. For example, if we observe Jonny Wilkinson, the English rugby union fly half, before he takes a kick for goal he takes a series of very deliberate steps to prepare himself. We see him putting down the ball and taking several steps backwards, then he turns sideways and stares at the ball, he then stares at the goal posts. Then he mentally rehearses his kick – he closes his eyes and we see him making small jerking movements; at this point he runs up and kicks the ball.

This is a personal performance routine and we see it with golfers, high jumpers, long jumpers and many other sports people. They have a set routine they follow every time they perform and it may include some of the following psychological techniques:

- attention control
- concentration

- relaxation
- imagery
- mental rehearsal
- self-talk.

Concentration is a vital aspect of any sports performance, as one lapse in concentration can mean the difference between success and failure. This was aptly demonstrated in the World Cup final by the German goalkeeper, Oliver Kahn, who had been outstanding in six games, but one fumble in the final presented a scoring chance to Ronaldo, who happily took it.

Concentration involves two important factors.

1. **Relevant environmental cues** – Information present in the game which is relevant to the athlete's performance; for example, the information that is relevant to a cricketer playing a stroke includes the ball, the movement of the bowler's hand, the flight and bounce of the ball and the position of the fielders. Irrelevant information includes noises from the crowd, the remarks of the fielders, the umpires and the weather. The batsman must focus on relevant cues to successfully play the delivery.
2. **Maintaining attentional focus** – Concentrating on the relevant cues and not being distracted by any outside distractions. Stephen Hendry is the most successful snooker player of all time, although some may argue not the most talented. However, on top of his talent he has the ability to stay focused throughout a match and not be distracted by the actions of other players, his own bad shots and the noise of the crowd.

Concentrating on information relevant to your sport is called an **associative attentional strategy**; however, some sports performers such as marathon runners, swimmers or long-distance cyclists find they compete better using a **dissociative attentional strategy**. This means that in order to take their mind off the pain and boredom they think about other things or imagine themselves elsewhere. The problem with this is that they may not be aware of the movements of their competitors or what is happening to their own energy levels and performance.

Take the following situations and work out what environmental information is relevant to the athlete's performance and what information is not relevant:

- a footballer taking a corner kick
- a sprinter preparing for a race
- a tennis player receiving a serve.

Self-talk is when you think about yourself and talk to yourself during a performance. For example, during a competition you may say 'that was a great shot' or 'what are you doing?' and this can affect your confidence levels. Positive self-talk helps you focus on the performance and stay in the present; it also helps you maintain concentration levels. Negative self-talk can distract from your performance and create negative emotions and self-doubts.

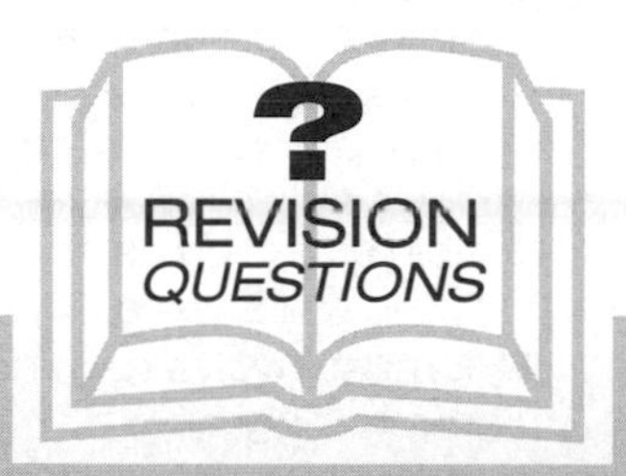

1) Explain why stress can be a positive force in our lives.
2) Discuss why stress is a problem for sports people and in general life.
3) Why are stressors specific to the individual?
4) What happens to the body whenever we become stressed?
5) Explain the terms 'arousal' and 'anxiety'.
6) Discuss three theories of arousal and performance.
7) What does Oxendine's taxonomy of sport explain?
8) Outline three methods of controlling stress.
9) Briefly describe how a psychologist can help an athlete prepare for a competition.

AGGRESSION

Aggression in sport seems to be becoming more and more commonplace, but in reality, aggressive acts in sport are becoming rarer. Witness some of the famous footballers of the 1970s and 1980s such as Tommy Smith, Ron 'Chopper' Harris, Norman 'bite yer legs' Hunter and Graeme Souness to see what aggressive play is really about. However, the media tend to sensationalise aggressive acts and give them plenty of coverage.

Psychologists have studied aggression over several years and asked the following questions:

- What do we mean by aggression?
- Why do sports people commit acts of aggression?
- What effect do these acts have on the outcome of the game?
- What can be done to prevent aggressive acts occurring?

065

1 Describe two occasions when you behaved aggressively on the sports field.
2 What caused you to be aggressive in this situation? Were you provoked? Was it to gain an advantage, or could you just not help it?
3 What effect did it have on the outcome of the game? Did it improve your chances of victory, have no effect, or decrease your chances of victory?

If you have never behaved aggressively, think of two occasions when you witnessed aggressive acts.

Discuss your answers with a partner and them contribute them to a class discussion.

Definitions

Aggression

In general life we refer to a range of behaviours where a person is being over zealous as being aggressive. Often these actions are mis-labelled.

Baron (1977) defined aggression as: '*any form of behaviour directed towards the goal of harming or injuring another person who is motivated to avoid such treatment.*'

In sport psychology aggression has a specific meaning: aiming to harm or injure an opponent to gain an advantage, rather than playing in a hard manner. Gill (1986) gives us four criteria which must all be met to allow us to label an action as aggressive.

1 There must be a physical or verbal behaviour.
2 It must involve causing harm or injury, whether it be physical or psychological.
3 It must be directed towards another living thing.
4 There must be the intention to cause harm or injury.

Look at the following examples and decide whether they are aggressive or not.

1 A footballer who has been hurt in a tackle kicks their opponent.
2 A runner elbows a competitor during an 800 m race in order to get in front of them.
3 A boxer lands a punch which knocks their opponent to the ground.
4 A rugby player tackles an opponent and lands on top of them, causing their ribs to be bruised.
5 A hockey player smashes their stick into an opponent's nose by mistake.
6 A bowler hits the batsman on the helmet with a bouncing delivery.
7 A rugby player tramples on an opponent's head in a ruck.
8 In going for a cross, two players collide causing a blood wound to each other's heads.
9 An ice hockey player swears at an opponent who makes an illegal challenge.
10 A tennis player kicks a ball away in a moment of rage.

Having looked at the situations in the activity we start to realise that aggression is a grey area. We cannot tell whether it is aggression unless we know the motives of the person who produces the action. Plenty of sports people get injured, but not necessarily through acts of aggression. In order to be more specific about this area we need to split aggressive acts into three distinct categories.

1. **Assertive acts** – When a person plays with high energy and emotion but within the rules of the game; for example, a footballer puts in hard, uncompromising tackles, or a tennis player is playing in a very tough and upbeat manner but always within the rules. This is assertive play because it is not intended to do any harm or cause any injury to their opponent, and uses force that is legitimate and within the rules.

2. **Instrumental aggression** – When acts of aggression are used to achieve a non-aggressive goal, such as improving a team's chances of victory, they are not usually accompanied by feelings of anger. For example, if you target the opposition's star player for rough treatment by one of your team, but you are willing to accept the punishment, then you are committing instrumental aggression. This also explains the sport of boxing, where the aim is to hurt your opponent to win the fight, rather than because you do not like your opponent. Also, in a rugby scrum, ruck or maul players use a legitimate amount of force, but this may actually harm or injure an opponent.

3. **Hostile aggression** – An act where the primary goal is to inflict harm or injury on an opponent purely for the sake of it, usually accompanied by feelings of anger. It often occurs when an individual is continually blocked from achieving a goal and their frustration and anger build up. For example, if a player is continually fouled or verbally abused they may eventually respond aggressively as a result.

STUDENT ACTIVITY

Go back to the previous activity and, based on the above information, categorise each action as assertive, instrumental or hostile aggression.

Theories of aggression

1. Instinct theory

This theory says that all people have an instinctive, inborn need or tendency to be aggressive. This theory is based on the work of Sigmund Freud in the early twentieth century. He said that man has two basic needs: the need to be aggressive and the need to have sex. He saw aggression as an innate instinct to ensure survival of human beings. It can be directed towards another person or it can be displaced. This release of aggression is called **catharsis**. People will say they play rugby or football at the weekend to get rid of the tension and aggression that builds up during the week. Other people will go swimming or running to achieve the same release of aggressive tendencies in a socially acceptable manner. This theory has also been used to explain why people fight at football matches as an outlet for their aggression, albeit it in a less socially acceptable manner.

There is little research to support this theory, and it cannot explain why some people are more aggressive than others. Indeed, you may know some people who never show aggressive behaviours. It also differs across cultures and this suggests there must be external influences which make the chances of aggression more likely.

2. Frustration–aggression theory

This theory states that aggression is the direct result of frustration that has built up due to goal blockage or failure. This theory was first proposed by Dollard *et al.* (1939), who claimed frustration would always produce aggression. However, in 1993 Berkowitz refined this theory by saying that frustration will lead to anger rather than aggression, particularly if we feel we have been unfairly treated, but we will not always produce an aggressive action. He went on to say that an aggressive action is more likely if aggressive cues are present (things related to aggression), but a person may be able to control their anger.

Social learning theory

This theory says that aggression is learnt through modelling and imitative behaviour, rather than being an inborn instinct. Albert Bandura (1973) conducted research involving groups of children watching groups of adults playing with a doll. The children who watched the adults punching and beating up the doll produced this reaction more than the group who watched the adults playing passively with the doll. This aggressive behaviour was increased when the children were positively rewarded for their actions.

Ice hockey has attracted a lot of research due to the regularity of fighting and fouling in the sport. Smith (1988) found that the violence in the game is the result of young amateur players modelling the professionals' behaviour.

It is easy to see how a young footballer may learn to be aggressive; at a football match he sees a player making hard tackles, some of which are illegal and dangerous, and being cheered on by the crowd and his coach. The harder the player tackles the more praise he gets and he develops a following by the fans who like this type of player. The young footballer learns that this is a positive way to behave and mimics the play in his own matches.

Research has shown that aggressive acts are more likely to be imitated if produced by a person of the same sex and if they are witnessed live rather than on television or in cartoon form.

Social learning theory is a very convincing theory, and we can see how the levels of aggression in sport are accompanied by rises in the level of violence in society, particularly on television and in films. However, it fails to explain how people can witness the same events and yet the majority of them will not produce an aggressive response, while a minority will mimic the behaviour. For example, a boxing match will have a cathartic effect on some supporters and will cause an aggressive response in others. It comes back to personality type and brings in the instinct theory.

Aggression–performance relationship

The research on the aggression–performance relationship is mixed. Widmeyer (1984) found aggressive behaviour improved performance, while Gill (1986) found it had no effect. Research in Belgian football by Lefebre and Passer (1974) into 240 games found that losing teams received more yellow cards for fouls than winning teams; Underwood and Whitwood (1980) showed no difference in fouls committed by winning and losing teams in the English First Division. Studies into ice hockey have shown that defending players commit more fouls than attacking players. Young (1993) found that violence in contact sports has increased recently as a results of the increasing rewards on offer and increasing professionalism in sport. While the relationship is unclear, we can predict that aggression is more likely to occur in certain situations than in others. For example, Leith (1991) and Cox (1998) say that aggressive acts are more likely to occur if a team is losing, their opponents are aggressive, the crowd is hostile and emotions are running high. Volkamer's (1972) research into football found the lower a team was in the league, and if they were playing away from home, then the more aggression they showed. Russell and Drury (1976) found the highest levels of aggression in the teams just behind the leaders.

Ultimately, the relationship between aggression and performance is unclear. It seems that some aggressive acts pay off while others do not. To summarise the research we can make the following points:

- aggression can increase levels of arousal which may be good or may be bad, depending on how high the arousal was initially
- aggression can improve team cohesion, as the team may become supportive of the aggressor or the opposition may become intimidated
- aggressive acts may receive negative reinforcement (sendings off, suspensions) which may have a detrimental effect on performance
- aggression can cause distractions from the game and therefore affect performance negatively.

Buy a copy of a newspaper that publishes tables of the disciplinary records of football teams (*Sports First* or a tabloid). Compare the position of each team in the league to their position in the discipline league, and answer the following questions.

1. Is there any relationship?
2. Are the most aggressive teams at the top or the bottom of the league table?
3. Are they at the top due to their aggression or are they aggressive because they are at the bottom?
4. In general, from your own experiences, do you think successful teams commit more or fewer aggressive acts?

Preventing aggression in young athletes

As a coach or a player it is possible to influence the number of aggressive acts players or team-mates commit. These approaches can be used to prevent aggressive play by young athletes or to re-educate those athletes who display aggressive behaviours.

1. Present non-aggressive role models for players to live up to. The perfect role model was Gary Lineker who was never riled and never retaliated no matter what punishment defenders gave him.
2. Punish severely acts of aggression. The various governing bodies are now taking aggressive acts very seriously and imposing long bans. The Rugby Football Union has taken steps to cite players who behave aggressively after a match and then punish them if they deem it necessary.
3. Punish coaches or teams as a whole who encourage aggressive play. This is done through fines or suspended fines.
4. Practice emotional control by teaching athletes how to manage their tempers, such as counting to ten before saying or doing anything. Relaxation techniques can also help here.
5. Limit external stimuli which are capable of provoking aggressive acts. If you know an athlete is vulnerable in certain situations or against certain teams, then consider whether you can prevent them going into that situation. For example, local derby matches are particularly heated affairs and often result in either player or crowd aggression.

STUDENT ACTIVITY

In the role of a sport psychologist, draw up a contract between yourself and a player you know. You must state which behaviours you want to eliminate, what you will do to help, the punishment for breaking the contract and the rewards for fulfilling the contract.

6 Contracting. A sport psychologist may attempt to minimise their athlete's aggressive behaviour by using a contract stating which behaviours the athlete is trying to minimise. In return, the psychologist will suggest a course of action they can offer to help. Also the sanctions for breaking the contract and reward for adhering to the contract will be stated The contract is agreed and signed by both parties.

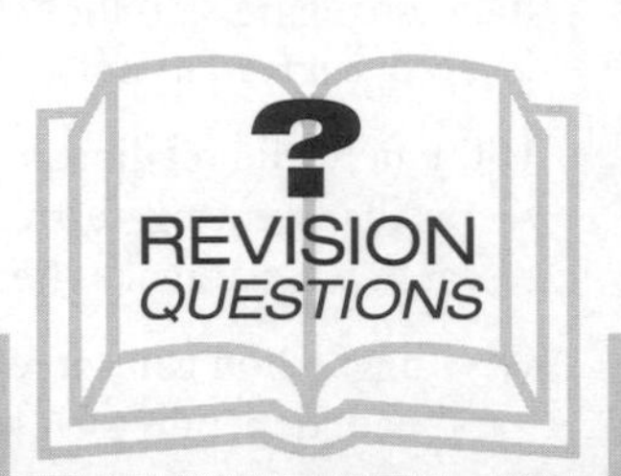

1) Explain what is meant by the term 'aggression'.
2) Explain the four criteria used by Gill to label an act as 'aggressive'.
3) Using examples, explain the difference between assertive behaviour, instrumental aggression and hostile aggression.
4) Briefly explain the three theories of aggression.
5) Explain which theory works best for you and why.
6) Do you think sport is a socially acceptable way for people to release their aggression?
7) Explain the relationship between aggression and performance.
8) Are there certain situations when aggression is more likely to occur than others?
9) What can be done to minimise the number of aggressive acts committed by children in contact sports?

MOTIVATION

If a sport psychologist were asked why athletes of similar talents achieve different levels of performance, they would consider several factors, such as personality and ability to cope with stress. However, if one subject could be said to influence everything in sport psychology it would be motivation – the reasons why we do what we do and behave and respond in the manner particular to us.

Psychologists would say that there is a reason for everything we do in life, and some of these motives are conscious and some are subconscious; as a result it can be difficult to assess our own motivating factors, let alone anyone else's.

Motivation is important to coaches and managers as they seek to get the best performances out their athletes. Kevin Keegan and Alex Ferguson are two managers who are also seen as being great motivators of people.

Motivation can be a difficult subject to pin down and deal with, because it is not steady and constant and depends on many factors. Most people will experience fluctuations in motivation in that some days they are fully prepared for the competition mentally, and on other days they just cannot seem to get themselves in the right frame of mind. This applies to all things we may do in a day, as sometimes it takes all our powers of motivation just to get out of bed!

Definitions

Motivation

Here are a number of definitions of motivation as put forward by various psychologists: '*Motive – the desire to fulfil a need*' (Cox, 1998).

Cox sees motivation as our behaviour being influenced by our needs and meeting these needs. Sage (1977) gives a more detailed definition: '*The internal mechanisms and external stimuli which arouse and direct behaviour*'.

This definition considers that motivation is produced by factors inside our bodies (or brains) and factors external to ourselves. However, these stimuli cause our arousal levels to rise and this influences our behaviour in certain ways.

Miller's (1967) definition expands on these internal and external factors: '*The study of motivation is the study of all those pushes and prods – biological, social or psychological that defeat our laziness and move us, either eagerly or reluctantly to action.*'

This definition takes a slightly pessimistic view of human beings: that we are essentially lazy and without pushes and prods would be inclined to do nothing. However, it makes the important point that rather than being motivated by one big thing, we are usually motivated by many small things which push and prod us into action.

STUDENT ACTIVITY

Consider each of the following statements made by athletes as to why they are motivated and decide whether it is an intrinsic or extrinsic motivating factor.

I want to win medals.
I want to earn an England cap.
I want to reach my full potential.
I want to make money.
I want to play in a good team.
I want to play in front of large crowds.
I want to give the public enjoyment.
I want to feel good about my performance.
I want to be recognised by the public for my ability.
I want to feel mastery in my own ability.
I want to feel the joy of winning.

Intrinsic and extrinsic motivation

To expand on Sage's definition, we can see motivation as coming from internal mechanisms or sources inside the body. We can call these **intrinsic factors**, or rewards coming from the activity itself. These include motives such as fun, pleasure, enjoyment, feelings of self-worth, excitement and self-mastery. They are the reasons why we do a sport and keep doing it.

The external stimuli can also be called the **extrinsic rewards** and they come from sources outside the activity. This would include the recognition and praise we get from other people, such as our coach, friends and family. It could also be the approval we get from the crowd who support us. For example, footballer Matthew Le Tissier said he is motivated by seeing the fans going away happy at the end of the match. Extrinsic motivating factors would also include trophies, medals, prizes, records and any money derived from success.

Initially, most people are motivated by intrinsic factors such as fun and enjoyment, however, their motivation can be changed and enhanced by the addition of extrinsic factors. Even professional footballers who gain huge extrinsic rewards from their sport will have started for the love of the game, but would they still play the game if you took their extrinsic rewards (their pay cheques) away from them?

STUDENT ACTIVITY

Consider the following story to further understand the complex relationship between intrinsic and extrinsic rewards.

> Every evening two young lads play tennis against the walls of a block of flats for two hours. Inside, Mrs Jones is trying to watch her favourite television programmes and is disturbed by the constant bouncing of the ball against her wall. So she hatches a plan to stop the boys playing. She tells the boys that because she likes to hear them playing tennis she will pay them £1 a day to play tennis against her wall. However, after a week she says she is running out of money and can only afford 50p a day. The boys are unconcerned and keep playing and collecting their money. After another week Mrs Jones says she can now only afford 20p a day. At this the boys become angry and tell Mrs Jones that it was not worth their effort to play for 20p a day, so they will not be coming back. Now Mrs Jones can watch her programmes in peace.

How can you explain this story in terms of intrinsic and extrinsic motivation? Can you relate this to professional sports people?

Achievement motivation

'I do not play to win, I play to fight against the idea of losing' (Eric Cantona, Manchester United, 1997).

Achievement motivation is seen as a personality factor and describes our persistence to keep striving for success, irrespective of the bad experiences and obstacles that are put in our way. It can be seen as our level of 'competitiveness' or desire for success. To watch the progress of long-distance athlete, Paula Radcliffe, is to see a person driven by a deep desire to be successful. She has a gruelling training schedule to make up for any shortcomings she is perceived to have, and finally she found the success her efforts deserve, winning the 2002 London Marathon.

Achievement motivation is not that simple, as the quote from Eric Cantona shows. Some people are driven to success and have no fear of failure, while other people are driven to succeed because they have a deep-rooted fear of failure. This paradox was addressed by McClelland and Atkinson in their theory of need achievement.

When in a certain sporting situation, we may have conflicting feelings: on one hand, we want to take part and achieve success, on the other hand, we are motivated to avoid the situation by our need to avoid failure. The relative strength of these emotions influences our achievement motivation:

achievement motivation =
need to achieve (nACH) – need to avoid failure (naF)

If our nACH outweighs our naF, then we are said to be high in achievement motivation; if our naF outweighs our nACH, we are said to be low in achievement motivation. This will influence our behaviour in sport and the types of challenges we seek.

A sports person with a high need to achieve will choose competitive situations and opponents close to their skill level who will challenge them. A person with a high fear of failure will choose opponents of much higher skill or much lower skill because these are less threatening to them; they will also tend to avoid situations involving personal challenges.

The situation will also affect achievement motivation. If the probability of success is high, it tends to weaken the need to achieve because the reward for success is low; on the other hand, if the probability of success is low and failure is likely, it tends to weaken the need to avoid failure. We can see this in the FA Cup, where non-league football teams play Premiership teams, and the outcome is often closer than it should be. For example, Dagenham and Redbridge nearly beat Charlton Athletic in 2001. This is because there is no real motive for success for the big team and thus no real reward because success is expected; for the smaller team, failure is expected so the value of success is massive. In terms of achievement motivation, the Premiership team is motivated to avoid failure, while the non-league team is motivated to achieve.

Weiner's attribution theory

Think of the following situations:

- You play well, but lose to an opponent who is better than you.
- You play well and beat a tough opponent.
- You play badly, and still manage to win against a weak opponent.
- You play badly and lose to an opponent you know you can beat.

1. Number the situations from 1 to 4 starting with the one which you find most satisfying (1), and ending with the one which you find least satisfying (4).
2. Take the situation ranked first, and explain why it is most satisfying. Why may this result have occurred?
3. Take the situation ranked fourth, and explain why it is least satisfying. Why may this result have occurred?

The reasons we give for an outcome are called attributions. We are attributing that outcome to a certain factor. We all make attributions about our own performances as well as those of other people. It is important for us to make attributions because:

- they affect our motivation levels
- we need to understand the outcome so that we can learn from our experiences
- they will affect our future expectations of success and failure.

Attributions fall into four categories:

1. **Ability or skill** – A performer's capability in performing skills.
2. **Effort** – The amount of physical or mental effort put into a task.
3. **Task difficulty** – The problems posed by the task, e.g. strength of the opposition or difficulty of a move.
4. **Luck** – Factors attributed to chance, such as the effect of the weather, the referee or the run of the ball.

As shown in Table 3.2, these can be classified as internal (inside an individual); external (outside the individual); stable (not subject to change); unstable (continually changing).

Table 3.2 Locus of control

	internal	external
stable	ability	task difficulty
unstable	effort	luck

STUDENT ACTIVITY

Look at the following statements and decide which of the four attributions' categories each one fits into.

Reasons for success

'I played well today, the training is paying off'

'I think I've got a natural talent for running – it comes easily to me'

'I tried like mad in the final set – that's what pulled me through'

'I was lucky to get away with that one'

Reasons for failure

'I played like an idiot! I deserved to lose'

I can't play this game – it's impossible'

'I was really lazy today'

'I didn't get the rub of the green today'

Now that you know what attributions are, do a piece of your own research. Look through the newspapers on Monday morning and try to find the reasons sports people and coaches give for their success or failures. Also, think why they are choosing to make these particular attributions.

Research findings

Research shows that winners tend to give internal attributions and take responsibility for their successes. They will usually say 'I won because I tried hard' or, 'I am more talented'. Losers, on the other hand, tend to give external attributions and distance themselves from their failures. For example, they will say 'the task was too difficult' or 'the referee was against me'. These attributions can be seen as ego enhancing and ego protective respectively. Winners give internal attributions to make themselves feel even better about themselves and losers give external attributions so they don't feel so bad.

Attributions and self-confidence

If we make a more stable attribution, i.e. to ability or task difficulty, it is more realistic and gives a clearer indication of future expectations and confidence. However, attribution to unstable factors can act to protect the ego and reduce loss of self-confidence.

This is important because confidence levels will influence motivation – the more confidence we have the more motivation we will have for a task.

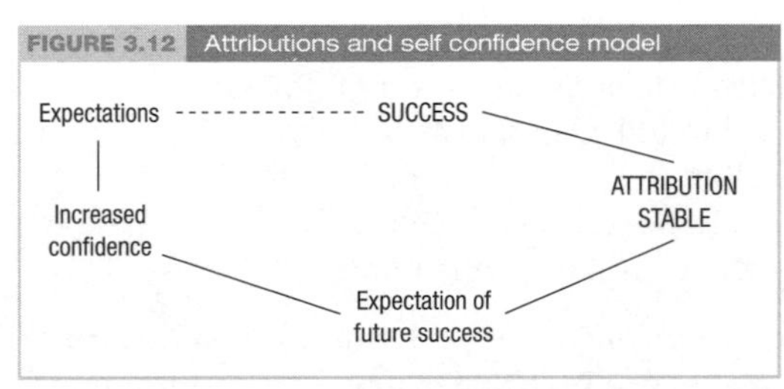

From S.5 Bull, (1991)

Learned helplessness

In the 1960s, experiments were done on animals to test the phenomenon of learned helplessness. Animals were put in a maze and given an electric shock to make them move. They tried to find their way out, but there was no exit. When they were put into a second maze they did not bother to find the way out. They had learnt to be helpless: learned helplessness.

This happens in sport: when a first experience is negative, the athlete will continue to expect the experience to be negative, thinking, for example 'I am rubbish at Badminton and never will be any good', 'What's the point, it won't work'.

STUDENT ACTIVITY

How can attribution theory prevent learned helplessness?

There are problems if athletes attribute an outcome incorrectly, as it affects future expectations of success. For example, if a team has beaten a better team due to the amount of effort they have expended and they attribute this correctly, then they will continue to play energetically in the next game. However, if they incorrectly attribute it to ability, then in the next game they may lose the ingredient that made them successful. We can see this happen in football when teams in the lower half of the league go on a winning streak of four or five matches that suddenly comes to an end. This is because they have started to believe that they are actually a team high in ability, rather than a team of average ability who are trying very hard. Once the effort goes, they start to lose again.

Participation motivation

Many people in Britain have been persuaded to start exercising as they are aware of the benefits of exercise. People are also persuaded by impressive facilities and the atmosphere of these centres.

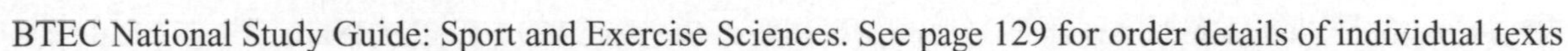

To further understand exercise adherence do the following.

1 Compile a list of reasons people give for taking up exercise/joining a gym.
2 Compile a list of reasons people give for:
a) not exercising
b) giving up their exercise programmes.

However, after six months, 55% of people who start an exercise programme have given up, but if a person carries on beyond nine months they are 90% likely to keep exercising long term. This is a question of motivation – once the motivation is lost then people drop out of their fitness programmes. We call the ability of people to stick to their programmes '**exercise adherence**'.

Strategies to prevent dropout and promote adherence to exercise programmes

1 **Setting goals and targets** – In order to direct an individual's efforts and to give them something to work for we can set them goals. However, this has to be done with great care so as not to negatively affect motivation. To help us do this we can use the acronym SMART:

   Specific goals – related to a particular aspect of fitness
   Measurable – the goal must be quantifiable
   Achievable – the goal must not be set too high
   Realistic – the goal must be realistically achievable
   Time constrained – there must be a time frame

   Goals can be set in the long term and the short term. A long-term goal may be achived over the course of a year, and can be broken down into shorter-term goals, such as one-month, three-month or six-month goals. We can use **outcome goals** which are related to the final result and **process goals** which are goals we can meet to help us achieve the outcome goal. For example, if a person's outcome goal is to lose 3% body fat over a three-month period, their process goal may be to exercise three times a week for the first month.

2 **Using a decision balance sheet** – An individual writes down all the gains they will make by exercising and all the things they may lose through taking up exercise. Hopefully the gains will outweigh the losses and this list will help to motivate them at difficult times.

3 **Prompts** – An individual puts up posters or reminders around the house which will keep giving them reminders to exercise. This could also be done with little coloured dots on mirrors or other places where they regularly look.

4 **Rewards for attendance/completing goals** – The individual is provided with an extrinsic reward for completing the goal or attending the gym regularly. This may be something to pamper themselves, such as a free massage, and should not be something that conflict with the goal – such a slap-up meal!

5 **Social support approaches** – You can help people exercise regularly by developing a social support group of like-minded people with similar fitness goals, so that they can arrange to meet at the gym at certain times. This makes it more difficult for people to miss their exercise session. Also, try to gain the backing of people they live with to support them rather than tease or criticise them.

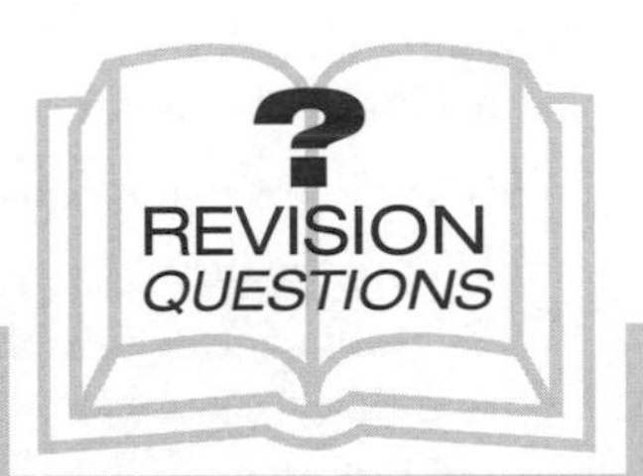

1) Define the term 'motivation'.
2) Explain the difference between intrinsic and extrinsic motivation.
3) Is it possible for a person's motivation to change? Why might this happen?
4) Explain how achievement motivation can influence the types of challenge a person may choose.
5) Why is it important to make attributions?
6) What is meant by the locus of control dimension in attribution theory?
7) What is meant by the stability dimension in attribution theory?
8) Do winners and losers make different types of attribution?
9) What is leaned helplessness?
10) What is meant by the term 'adherence'?
11) How can a psychologist help people adhere to their exercise programmes?

GROUP DYNAMICS

Group processes

Throughout our sporting and social lives we are involved in working in groups, such as our families, our school groups, our friendship groups and the sports teams we play in. Sports teams have different characteristics; for example, an athletics team will have different teamwork demands to a rugby team or a cricket team. However, all groups rely on the fundamental characteristic of teamwork.

Defining a group is not easy, however, the minimum number required for a group is two people. A group can be seen as two or more like-minded people interacting to produce an outcome they could not achieve on their own. Groups involve interaction or working with other people in order to influence the behaviour of other people and in turn be influenced by them.

Definitions

Group

To define a group we can use the distinguishing characteristics of groups as devised by Weinberg and Gould (1995). A group should have

- a oollootivo idontity
- a sense of shared purpose or objectives
- structured modes of communication
- personal and/or task interdependence
- interpersonal attraction.

Opinion is divided on whether groups are really more effective than individuals. Look at the following contradictory sayings:

Two heads are better than one	vs.	Too many cooks spoil the broth
The more the merrier	vs.	Three is a crowd
If you want a job done well do it yourself	vs.	A jack of all trades is the master of none
There is strength in numbers	vs.	A chain is as strong as its weakest link

(from A. V. Carron, 1988)

So why is the outcome of the group not always equal to the sum of its parts? For example, we can see in football that the teams with the best players do not always get the results they should. Chelsea have often been criticised as underachieving, as they have had some of the best European talent and yet not managed to challenge for the Premiership trophy. In the season 1996–97, Middlesborough had outstanding players such as Juninho, Fabrizio Ravanelli and Emerson and yet they ended the season being relegated. At the 1996 Olympic Games, the brilliant sprinters of the USA were beaten in the 4 × 100 m relay by the unfancied Canadian team. Groups do not always achieve what they should due to the following:

- communication difficulties
- co-ordination of the group
- lack of motivation
- laziness or reduced effort.

Stages of group development

A group of people coming together does not form a team. Becoming a team demands a process of development. Tuckman (1965) proposed a four-stage model of group development:

- forming
- storming
- norming
- performing.

Each group will go through the four stages; however, the length of time they spend in each stage is variable.

Forming

The group comes together, with individuals meeting and familiarising themselves with the other members of the group. The structure and relationships within the group are formed and tested. If it is a team, the coach may develop strategies or games to 'break the ice' between the group members.

Storming

A period of conflict will follow the forming stage as individuals seek their roles and status within the group. This may involve conflict between individual members, rebellion against the leader or resistance to the way the team is being developed or managed or the tactics they are adopting. This is also a period of intense inter-group competition, as group members compete for their positions within the team.

Norming

Once the hostility and fighting has been overcome, either by athletes leaving the group or accepting the common goals and values of the group, a period of norming occurs. Here, the group starts to cooperate and work together to reach common goals. The group pulls together and the roles are established and become stable.

Performing

In the final stage, the group members work together to achieve their mutual goals. The relationships within the group have become well established, as have issues of leadership and strategies for play. It is unrealistic to see the group as being stable and performing in a steady way. The relationships within the group will change and develop with time, sometimes for the good of the group and sometimes to its detriment. As new members join the group there will be a new period of storming and norming, as this person is either accepted or rejected. This re-evaluation of the group is often beneficial, and stops the group becoming stale. Successful teams seem to be settled and assimilate two or three new players a year to keep them fresh. Bringing in too many new players can disrupt the group and change the nature of the group completely.

It is interesting to see how Manchester United developed through the 1990s. They had a large influx of new players who had come up through the youth and reserve sides into the first team, and because they were already familiar with the group norms and expectations they became successful fairly quickly. Each year they bought in two or three new players to keep things fresh and keep the group developing. Their least successful season in 2001–02 was blamed on the introduction of Juan Sebastien Veron, who was seen to disrupt group dynamics and reduce the team's effectiveness.

Group effectiveness

The aim of a group is to be effective by using the strengths of each person to better the effectiveness of the group. However, the outcome is often not equal to the sum of its parts.

Steiner (1972) proposes a model of group effectiveness:

$$\text{Actual productivity} = \text{Potential productivity} - \text{Process losses}$$

Where: actual productivity = the actual performance achieved
potential productivity = the best possible performance achievable by that group based on its resources (ability, knowledge, skills)
process losses = losses due to working as part of a group (co-ordination losses, communication problems, losses in motivation)

For example, in a tug of war team each member can pull 100 kg on their own; as a team of four they pull 360 kg in total. Why do you think this would happen?

Social loafing

One of the problems of working in groups is that it tends to affect motivation. People do not seem to work as hard in groups when compared with working on their own. Research shows that rowers in larger teams give less effort than smaller teams:

1 person = 100% effort
2 people = 90% effort
4 people = 80% effort
8 people = 65% effort

This phenomenon is called the **Ringelman effect** or **social loafing** and is defined as the tendency of individuals to lessen their effort when part of a group.

Research done into social loafing

1 Relationship between group size and rope-pulling performance.

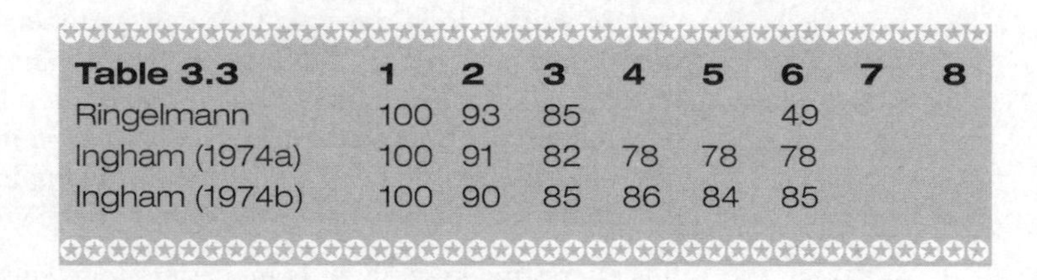

Table 3.3	1	2	3	4	5	6	7	8
Ringelmann	100	93	85			49		
Ingham (1974a)	100	91	82	78	78	78		
Ingham (1974b)	100	90	85	86	84	85		

2 Latane, Williams and Harkins (1980) used a hand-clapping task:

1 person clapping – 100%
2 people clapping – 71%
4 people clapping – 51%
6 people clapping – 40%

3 Latane and Hardy (1988) found that cheerleaders produced 94% as much noise when in pairs as when performing alone.

Why does social loafing occur?

1 Being part of a group reduces identifiability and accountability. The individuals may not feel that their efforts can be identified and thus that people will not know how hard they worked.

2 Athletes may feel working hard in a group does not bring recognition. We all like to gain recognition for our hard work and therefore, if there is no chance of this, we may not be so concerned about being successful.

3 Athletes may feel they do not need to work hard as team-mates will take up the slack. We realise that if people do not know how little or how much effort we are putting in there are always other people who will do the work for us. This often happens when a team contains a 'star' player;

we think we can let them do the work or, if we give them the ball, they will win the match for us.

STUDENT ACTIVITY

How can social loafing be minimised?

1 Give examples from your own experience of social loafing.
2 How does social loafing occur in the following sports and what strategies can be used to prevent social loafing occurring?
   a) 4 × 100 m or 4 × 400 m relay
   b) eight-person rowing race
   c) rugby scrummage
   d) doubles in tennis
   e) football.

Hint: think about how performances can be quantified (put into figures) or how individual performance can be identified.

Cohesion

Cohesion is concerned with the extent to which a team is willing to stick together and work together.

The forces mentioned in the definition will tend to cover two areas:

- the attractiveness of the group to individual members
- the extent to which members are willing to work together to achieve group goals.

To be successful in its goals, a group has to be cohesive. The extent to which cohesion is important depends upon the sport and the level of interaction needed.

Student activity

Place the following ten team sports in order depending upon the level of interaction and thus cohesion needed to be successful.

Rowing eights	Tennis doubles	4 × 100 m relay
Golf team	Bobsleigh four	Cricket team
Volleyball team	Cycling team	Curling team
Synchronised swimming team		

Definitions

Cohesion is defined by Festinger *et al.* (1950) as *'the total field of forces which act on members to remain in the group.'*

Types of cohesion

There seem to be two definite types of cohesion within a group.

- **Task cohesion** – The willingness of a team to work together to achieve their goals.
- **Social cohesion** – The willingness of the team to socialise together.

It would appear that task cohesion comes first as this is why the team has formed in the first place. If the group is lucky they will find that they develop social cohesion as well, and this usually has a beneficial effect on performance. This is because if you feel good about your team-mates you are more likely to want success for each other as well as yourself.

However, history has shown many examples where individuals or groups which have no interpersonal attraction can still be successful. For example, Andy Cole and Teddy Sheringham formed an excellent striking partnership for

Manchester United while never being on speaking terms. There is the famous example of the East German rowing eight who won the Olympic gold medal in 1968 despite the fact that they could not stand each other's company; also the relationship between Steven Redgrave and Andrew Pinsent had been so tested by the time they won the Olympic gold medal in 1996 that they had decided the only way to carry on was to move up to a four-man crew, which meant that more relationships had to be developed.

In summary, the research says that cohesion is important in successful teams, but that task cohesion is more important than social cohesion. It does depend upon the sport being played, as groups that need high levels of interaction need higher levels of cohesion.

Research also suggests that success will produce increased cohesion rather than cohesion coming before performance. Being successful helps to develop feelings of group attraction, and this will help to develop more success, and so on. This can be seen by the cycle of success, in that once a team has been successful once they tend to continue being successful, i.e. success breeds success.

LEADERSHIP

Before reading the section on leadership, take time to answer the following questions.

1 How would you define 'leadership'?
2 Make a list of eight people you consider to be effective leaders. Choose four from sport and four from other areas.
3 List eight personality qualities or traits that you think are needed to make an effective leader.
4 Are the leadership qualities needed to lead in sport the same as in all leadership situations?
5 Do you think an effective leader will be effective in all situations? Why?

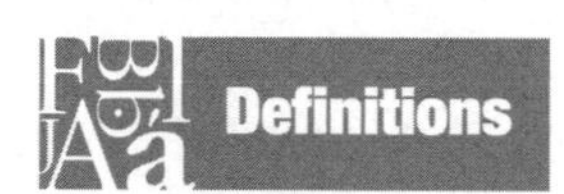

Leadership
Leadership can be defined in the following manner: '*The behavioural process of influencing individuals and groups towards goals*' (Barron, 1977)

Leadership in sport

The choice of a manager, coach or captain is often the most important decision a club's members have to make. They see it as crucial in influencing the club's chances of success. Great leaders in sport are held in the highest regard, irrespective of their talent on the pitch. Sports people such as Sven Goran Eriksson, Kevin Keegan, Martin Johnson, Nasser Hussain and Linford Christie are all regarded as 'great' leaders.

Leadership behaviour covers a variety of activities, hence we call it multidimensional, it includes:

- decision-making processes
- motivational techniques
- giving feedback
- establishing interpersonal relationships
- confidently directing the group.

Leaders are different from managers: managers plan, organise, budget, schedule, recruit; leaders determine how a task is completed.

People become leaders in different ways; not all are appointed. **Prescribed leaders** are appointed by a person in authority, e.g. a chairman appoints a manager, a manager appoints a coach, a principal appoints a teacher. **Emergent leaders** emerge from a group and take over responsibility. e.g. David Beckham emerged to become the leader of the England football team. Emergent leaders are often more effective as they have the respect of their group members.

Theories of leadership

Sport psychologists have sought to explain leadership effectiveness for many years and they have used the following theories to help understand effective leadership behaviour.

Trait approach

In the 1920s researchers tried to show that characteristics or personality traits were stable and common to all leaders. Thus, to be a good leader you needed to have intelligence, assertiveness, independence and self-confidence. Therefore, a person who is a good leader in one situation will be a good leader in all situations.

Behavioural approach

The trait approach says that leaders are 'born', but the behavioural approach says that anyone can become a good leader by learning the behaviour of effective leaders. Thus, this approach supports the view that leadership skills can be developed through experience and training.

Interactional approach

Trait and personal approaches look at personality traits. The interactional approach looks at the interaction between the person and the situation. It stresses the following points.

1. Effective leaders cannot be predicted solely on personality
2. Effective leadership fits specific situations, as some leaders function better in certain circumstances than others.
3. Leadership style needs to change to match the demands of the situation.

STUDENT ACTIVITY

What type of leadership (task-oriented or relationship-oriented) would be relevant in the following situations:

- A PE teacher
- A Premiership team captain
- A Member of Parliament
- Captain of over 50s badminton team
- A student leading a group in a presentation
- An aerobics teacher.

If you feel a mixture of the two styles would be appropriate, state what percentage of each would be needed.

For example, relationship-oriented leaders develop interpersonal relationships, provide good communication and ensure everyone is feeling good within the group. However, task-oriented leaders are concerned with getting the work done and meeting objectives.

The multidimensional model of sport leadership

The three models previously discussed were adapted from non-sporting examples. Although they help us understand leadership behaviour, each model has its shortcomings. In 1980, P. Chelladurai presented a sport-specific model. He proposed the view that effective leadership will vary depending on the characteristics of the athletes, the leader and the situation.

What does Figure 3.13 mean?

FIGURE 3.13 Leadership model

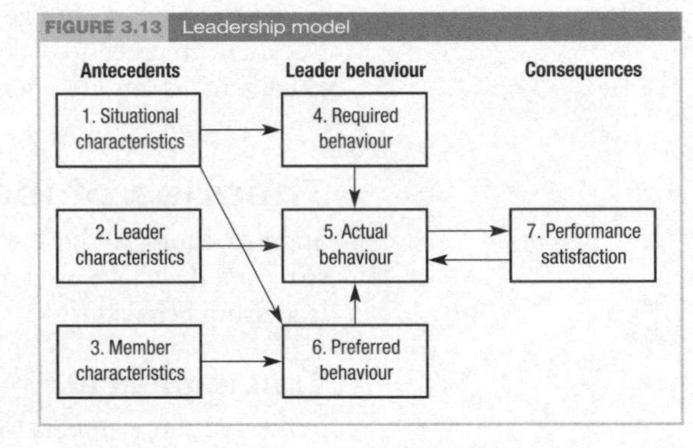

1. **Situational characteristics** – The characteristics such as size, type of sport, winning or losing, of the situation the group is in.
2. **Leader characteristics** – The personal qualities of the leader. Some of the qualities needed are confidence, intelligence, assertiveness and self-motivation.
3. **Member characteristics** – The different personality types of different groups of athletes, these characteristics include age, gender, ability level and experience.
4. **Required behaviour** – The type of behaviour required of a leader in a particular situation. For example, if a team is losing with five minutes to go, it is best for the leader to make a decision themselves rather than discuss it with their team-mates.
5. **Actual behaviour** – The behaviours the leader actually displays.
6. **Preferred behaviour** – The preferred leadership of the group, depending on their characteristics.
7. **Performance satisfaction** – The extent to which the group members are satisfied with the leader's behaviour and with the outcome of the competition.

The model says that if a leader behaves appropriately for the particular situation and these behaviours match the preferences of the group members, then they will achieve their best performance and feel satisfied.

The leadership scale for sport

The leadership scale for sport was developed by Chelladurai to assess the five main behaviours of coaches in their positions of leadership, and to evaluate how often they use each.

1. **Training and instruction** – Information is provided by the coach, aimed at improving the performance of the athlete in terms of technique and strategy.
2. **Democratic behaviour** – The athlete is involved in reaching decisions regarding group goals and group strategy.
3. **Autocratic behaviour** – The coach acts independently, forcing decisions on the group.
4. **Social support behaviour** – This is aimed at improving the wellbeing and welfare of the athletes and developing group relationships.
5. **Positive feedback behaviour** – This rewards individual and group actions through acknowledging athletes' efforts and performance.

Leadership in sport is a complex subject as it involves the process of influencing people towards achieving their personal goals and the goals of the group. Individuals will respond to different types of leader and different types of leadership behaviour. Different leaders have different strengths and ways of leading, and may find that what was successful in one situation is not so effective in another.

Take some time to consider the effect an audience has on you personally. How do you feel inside when performing in front of an audience? Does it improve or worsen your performance? Does it matter whether the audience is supportive or not, known or unknown to you, large or small?

Social facilitation
Zajonc (1965) defines social facilitation as: '*the consequences upon behaviour which derive from the sheer presence of other individuals*'

Social facilitation

Social facilitation is the change in performance that occurs due to the presence of others; whether the presence is an audience or fellow competitors.

There is no doubt that our performances change as the result of the presence of other people. Think about how you feel when your parents or friends come to watch you, or when you start to perform in front of an audience.

Zajonc (1965) defined the different types of people present, separating them into those people who are competing against you and those people who are merely present and not competing (Figure 3.14).

FIGURE 3.14 Social facilitation model

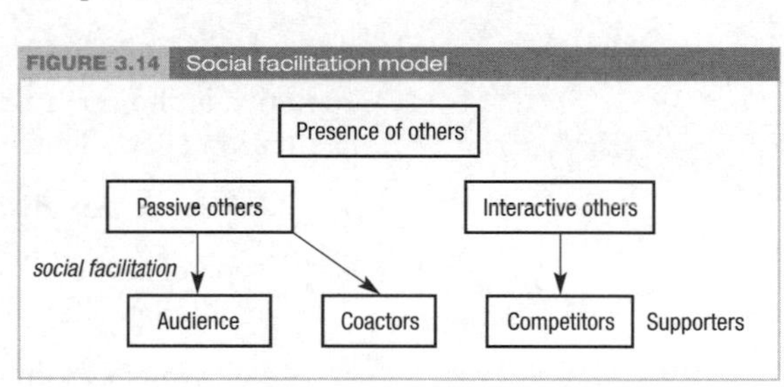

Coactors are people involved in the same activity, but not competing directly. Triplett (1898) did some of the earliest experiments in sport psychology. He examined coaction in the following three conditions, using cyclists: 1. unpaced; 2. paced (coactor on another bike); 3. paced competitive (coactors pacing and competing). His findings were that cyclists in condition 2 were 34 seconds per mile faster than cyclists in condition 1, while cyclists in condition 3 were 39 seconds per mile faster than cyclists in condition 1.

FIGURE 3.15 Zajonc's expanded model (1965)

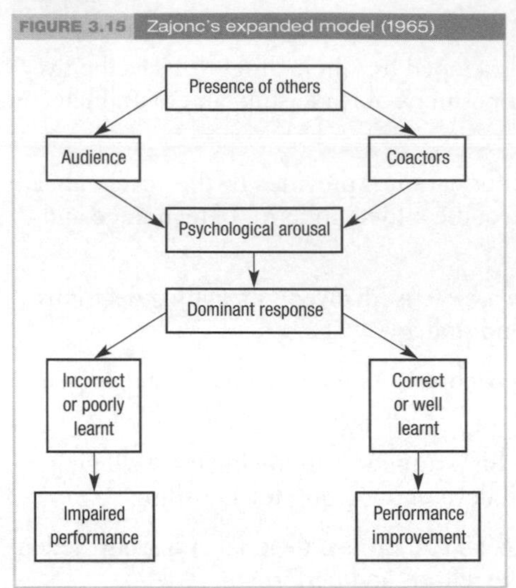

The reasons for social faciliation are not always clear; however, Triplett concluded that in his experiment it was due to the physical effects, such as suctioning and sheltering resulting from travelling behind another rider, and psychological effects such as encouragement, anxiety, pressure and competitiveness which are felt as the result of cycling with someone else. Triplett concluded that it did not matter if the cyclists were competing; what was important was that the: 'bodily presence of another rider is stimulus to a rider in arousing the competitive instinct'.

Zajonc's expanded model showed that whether the audience or coactors have a positive or negative effect on performance depends upon how well the skill has been learnt. A poorly learnt skill will become worse, while a well-learnt skill will be improved (Figure 3.15). This links in well with the effect of stress on performance, and it can be seen that the presence of others would cause more stress.

Zajonc also looked at the relationship between the audience effect and the standard of the performer. His results are shown in Figure 3.16.

FIGURE 3.16 Audience effect and the standard of performer

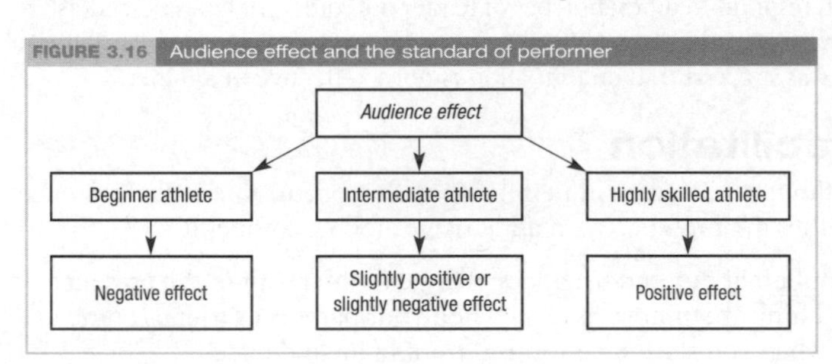

The effect also depends upon the nature of the task, i.e. whether it is strength or skill related. Strength tasks will usually be enhanced by the presence of others. However, skilled tasks (especially poorly learnt skills) may suffer. Social facilitation effects tend to disappear as the individual gets used to it.

Cottrell (1968) said that it is not the mere presence of an audience which creates arousal, but that the type of audience is also very important. For example, a blindfolded audience had no facilitation effect. The following factors will affect social facilitation.

1 **Audience expertise** – An expert audience will increase arousal level.

2 **Type of audience** – A **pro-winning** audience will have more of a facilitation effect than a **pro-enjoyment** audience.

3 **Performer's evaluation of the audience** – The performer decides what they think the audience wants and is aroused accordingly.

4 **Size** – A larger audience will have more of a facilitation effect.

Home advantage

Home advantage is the view that the team playing at home has a disproportionately high chance of winning in relation to the team playing away from home. This phenomenon was apparent in the World Cup of 2002 where the joint hosts South Korea and Japan both did far better than they had ever previously done, particularly South Korea, who progressed to the semi-finals.

STUDENT ACTIVITY

To see whether a home advantage does exist, take the sports supplement from a paper on Sunday or Monday and examine the results from three or four sports, such as football, rugby, hockey or cricket. Work out the following percentages:

- teams winning at home
- teams drawing at home
- teams losing at home.

1 Do your results support the theory of home advantage?
2 Would there be a home advantage in individual sports such as athletics, tennis or golf?

Why is there a home advantage?

There are many reasons why home teams are more successful; some of these are physical and some are psychological:

- familiarity with the surroundings and the surfaces
- a supportive home crowd who give positive approval
- less intimidation by opposing supporters
- the territory is theirs and claimed by display of their playing colours
- there is less travel involved in getting to the match
- travel can cause boredom and staleness
- players do not have to stay in unfamiliar surroundings and eat unfamiliar food
- home teams are more likely to play offensively
- away teams may not be treated well by their opponents
- referees and officials may unconsciously favour the home team to seek the crowd's approval.

Home advantage may be seen as being as a disadvantage to the away team rather than an advantage to the home team. It is the job of the coach and psychologist to find ways of minimising this away disadvantage.

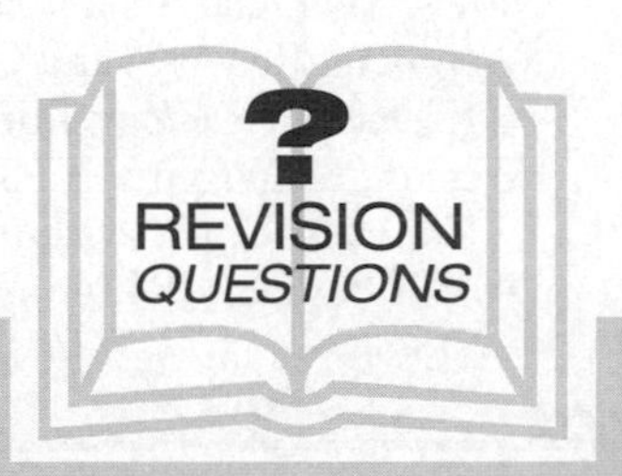

1) Explain what is meant by the term 'group'.
2) Outline the four stages of group development.
3) Explain Steiner's model of group effectiveness
4) What is meant by the term 'social loafing'?
5) How can social loafing be minimised?
6) What is cohesion? Describe the two types.
7) How important is cohesion in group performance?
8) Explain the three theories of leadership.
9) Discuss the multidimensional model of leadership and how it explains group success.
10) What is social facilitation and why does it exist?
11) Why do home teams seem to have an advantage due to playing at home?

1) Explain the relationship between personality and sports performance.
2) Discuss the view that people are motivated predominantly by material rewards.
3) Choose two different sports skills and explain how performance is affected by stressful situations.
4) Discuss the view that there is no such thing as an non-cohesive group.

FURTHER READING

There is a wealth of excellent texts available, either completely devoted to sport psychology or where sport psychology constitutes a large part. The following are recommended.

Beashel, P. and Taylor, J. (1996) *Advanced Studies in Physical Education and Sport*. Nelson
Davis, R. J., Bull, C. R., Roscoe, J. V., Roscoe, D.A. (2000) *Physical Education and the Study of Sport*. London: Mosby
Jarvis, Matt (2000) *Sport Psychology*. London: Routledge
Weinberg, Robert S. and Gould, Daniel (1995) *Foundations of Sport and Exercise Psychology*. Illinois: Human Kinetics
Wesson, K., Wiggins, N., Thompson, G., Hartigan, S. (2000) *Sport and P.E.: A Complete Guide to Advanced Level Study*. London: Hodder and Stoughton
Woods Barbara (1998) *Applying Psychology to Sport*. London: Hodder and Stoughton

REFERENCES

Bandura, A. (1977a) *Social Learning Theory*. Eaglewood Cliffs, NJ: Pentice-Hall.
Bandura, A. Self-efficacy: Toward a unifying theory of behavioural change. *Psychological Review*, 84, 191–215.
Beashel, P. and Taylor, J. (1996) *Advanced Studies in Physical Education and Sport*. Nelson.
Berkowicz, L. (1969) Roots of Aggression. Atherton Press.
Cattell, R. B. (1965) *The Scientific Analysis of Personality*. London: Penguin
Chelladurai, P. and Carron, A.V. (1978) Leadership. *Sociology of Sport Monograph Series*.
Cox, R. (1994) *Sports Psychology: Concepts and Applications*. 3rd Edition. Wm C. Brown Communications.

Davis, R. J. Bull, C. R. Roscoe, J. V. Roscoe, D. A. (2000) *Physical Education and the Study of Sport*. London: Mosby.

Dollard, J. Doob, J. Miller, N. Mowrer, O. and Sears, R. (1939) *Frustration and Aggression*. New Haven, Conneticut: Yale University Press.

Eysenck, H. J. and Eysenck, S. B. G. (1964) *Manual of Eysenck Personality Inventory*. University of London Press.

Fazey, J. and Hardy, L. (1988) The inverted U hypothesis: a catastrophe for sport psychology? *British Association of Sports Sciences Monograph*, no.1. NCF.

Hollander, E. P. (1971) *Principles and methods of Social psychology*, 2nd edition. Oxford University Press.

Jarvis, Matt (2000) *Sport Psychology*. London: Routledge.

Latane, B. Harkins, S. G. and Williams, K. D. (1980) *Many Hands make Light Work: Social Loafing as a Social Disease*. Unpublished manuscript. Columbus: Ohio State University.

Oxendine, C. B. (1970) Emotional Arousal and Motor Performance. *Quest*, 13, 23–30.

Triplett, N. (1898) The dynamogenic factors in pacemaking and competition. *American Journal of psychology*, 9, 507–533.

Weinberg, Robert S. and Gould, Daniel (1995) *Foundations of Sport and Exercise Psychology*. Illinois: Human Kinetics.

Wesson, K. Wiggins, N. Thompson, G. Hartigan S. (2000) *Sport and P.E.: A complete Guide to Advanced Level Study*. London: Hodder and Stoughton.

Zajonc, R. B. (1965) Social Facilitation. *Science*, 149, 269–274.

Woods, Barbara (1998) *Applying Psychology to Sport*. London: Hodder and Stoughton.

ANATOMY FOR SPORT AND EXERCISE

CHAPTER 7

This chapter introduces the biological principles of how the body moves, and includes a detailed exploration of the skeleton and neuromuscular systems. The anatomy and physiology of the cardiovascular and respiratory systems are also discussed.

By the end of this chapter students should be able to:

- understand the structure of the skeleton
- be aware of the different types of joint and the movements they permit
- have an understanding of the different types of muscle and how skeletal muscle contracts
- explain how the skeletal and neuromuscular systems act on the skeleton to produce movement
- have an understanding of the structure and function of the cardiovascular and respiratory systems.

THE SKELETON

At birth, the human skeleton is made up of 275 different bones. As the skeleton matures, some bones **fuse** together, leaving the average adult with a skeleton consisting of 206 bones.

The function of the skeleton is five-fold.

1. **Movement** – The skeleton plays an important part in movement by providing a series of movable **levers** to which muscles are attached. The muscles can then pull on these levers to move different parts of the body.
2. **Protection** – The skeleton protects important internal organs. For example, the cranium protects the brain. What do the ribs and sternum protect?
3. **Shape** – The skeleton provides the human with the basic framework that gives the body its particular form.
4. **Red and white blood cell production** – Red and white blood cells are produced from the skeletal bone marrow of certain bones.
5. **Mineral storage** – The bones store calcium and phospherus which can be used by the body when the diet does not supply adequate amounts.

FIGURE 7.1 Anterior view of the human skeleton

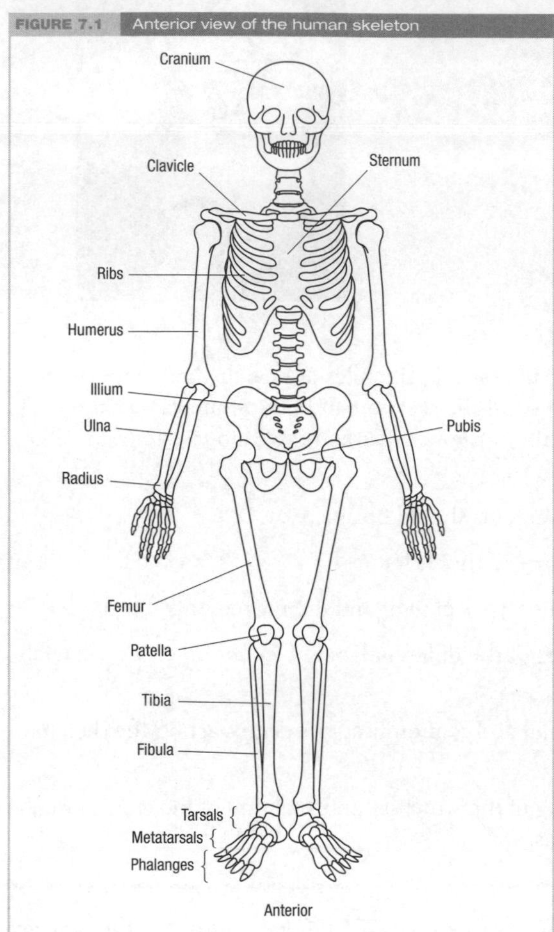

FIGURE 7.2 Posterior view of the human skeleton

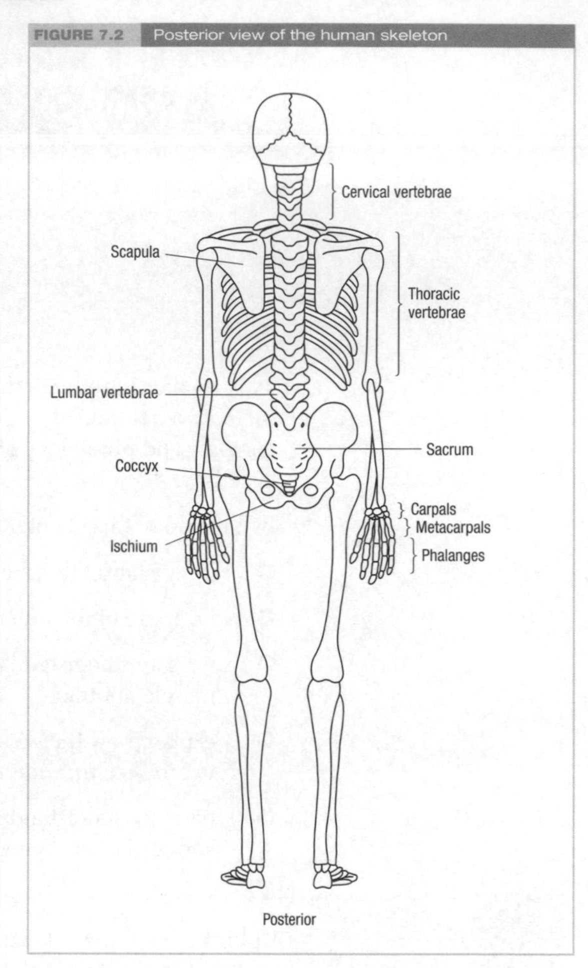

- **Skull** – This is the bony framework of the head and is made up of eight **cranial** bones (the cranium) and fourteen **facial** bones.
- **The chest** – This is made up of the **sternum** and the **ribs** and protects the heart and lungs. The sternum is a flat, dagger-shaped bone situated in the middle of the chest. The ribs are thin, flat, curved bones. There are 24 ribs in total, arranged in 12 pairs. The first seven pairs are connected to the spine at the back of the body and directly to sternum by cartilage at the front of the body. The next three pairs of are attached to the spine at the back of the body and to the rib above at the front of the body. The last two pairs are called floating ribs. They are attached to the spine but are not connected to anything at the front of the body.
- **Vertebral column** – The vertebral column is also known as the **spine**, the **backbone** or the **spinal column**. It consists of 33 vertebrae which are divided into five categories, depending on where they are located in the column. At the top of the vertebral column there are seven **cervical**

vertebrae. The first is called the **atlas** and the second is called the **axis**. The next twelve vertebrae are called the **thoracic** vertebrae. They are larger than cervical vertebrae and increase in size from top to bottom.The next five bones are called the **lumbar** vertebrae and are the largest vertebrae in the spinal column. They support the majority of the body's weight. The **sacrum** is located just below the lumbar vertebrae and consists of five fused bones. The bottom of the spinal column is called the **coccyx** or tailbone. It consists of four bones that are fused together.

- **Arm** – This consists of the **humerus**, **radius** and **ulna**. The humerus is in the upper arm and its head fits into the scapula in the shoulder. The lower arm consists of the radius and ulna. The radius is located on the side away from the body (lateral side) and the ulna is located on the side towards the body (medial side) when standing in the anatomical position. To help you remember this, the radius is in line with the thumb.
  The elbow is occasionally referred to as the funny bone. This is due to the tingling and often quite unpleasant and painful sensation caused by a blow to the ulnar nerve, which is located alongside the humerus bone. However, the feeling that results is usually not very humerous!
- **Hand** – The hand comprises three parts: the **wrist** the **palm** and **five fingers**, totalling 27 bones. The wrist is made up of eight small bones called the **carpal bones**. The palm consists of five **metacarpal bones**, one aligned with each of the fingers. The fingers are made up of 14 bones called **phalanges**.
- **Leg** – The thigh is composed of a single bone called the **femur**, which is the longest, largest, and strongest bone in the body. The lower leg consists of the **fibula** and the **tibia**. The tibia is also known as the shin-bone. The fibula is located on the lateral side of the body, and the tibia on the medial side. The tibia is larger than the fibula because it bears most of the weight. The **patella**, more commonly called the **kneecap** is a large, triangular bone located within a tendon between the femur and the tibia. It protects the knee joint and strengthens the tendon that forms the knee. The bones of the lower extremities are the heaviest, largest, and strongest bones in the body because they must bear the entire weight of the body when a person is standing in the upright position.
- **Foot** – This contains 26 bones and includes the **ankle**, the **instep** and **five toes**. The ankle is made up of seven **tarsal** bones. The **metatarsal** and **phalanges** bones of the foot are similar in number and position to the metacarpal and phalanges bones of the hand.
- **Shoulder girdle** – This is also known as the **pectoral girdle**. It is composed of four bones: two clavicles and two scapulae. The **clavicle**, more commonly called the **collarbone**, connects the humerus to the trunk of the body. One end of the clavicle is connected to the sternum and one end is connected to the scapula. The **scapula** is also called the **shoulder blade**. It is a large, triangular, flat bone located on the back of the rib cage. The head of the humerus fits into its shallow depression called the glenoid cavity. The primary function of the pectoral girdle is to provide an attachment point for the numerous muscles that allow the shoulder and elbow joints to move.

1 Look at the labelled diagram of the skeleton on page 164, then draw up a list of **all** the bones in:
a) the axial skeleton
b) the appendicular skeleton.
2 Shade the bones of the axial skeleton with one colour and all the bones of the appendicular skeleton with a different colour.

- **Pelvic girdle** – Also called the **hip girdle**, this part of the skeleton is made up of two **coxal** (hip) bones. The coxal bone consists of three separate parts: the **ilium**, the **ischium** and the **pubis**. The two coxal bones are connected at the front of the body by the pubic symphysis. At the back of the body they meet at either side of the sacrum. The pelvic girdle supports the weight of the body from the vertebral column and offers protection for the bladder, the reproductive organs, and the developing foetus in a pregnant woman.

The axial and appendicular skeleton

The skeleton is split into two different parts: the axial skeleton and the appendicular skeleton.

The axial skeleton consists of 80 bones and includes the cranium, ribs, sternum and vertebral column. The primary function of the axial skeleton is to protect the major organs in the body: the brain, heart, lungs and spinal cord.

The appendicular skeleton has 126 bones and is made up of the shoulder girdle, hip girdle, arms, hands, legs and feet. There are 64 bones in the shoulders and upper limbs and 62 in the pelvis and lower limbs. The main purpose of the appendicular skeleton is to work in conjunction with the muscular system to provide movement.

There are very few differences between the skeletons of the male and the female. Male bones are usually larger and heavier than the corresponding female bones. The female's pelvic cavity is wider than the male's in order to accommodate childbirth. Due to the biblical story of Adam and Eve, some people believe that males and females have a different number of ribs, but this is not true; both males and females have 24 ribs.

Bone

Bone is a living tissue that is continually being broken down and remade. Approximately every seven years your body will have replaced the equivalent of the whole of your skeleton!

Classification of bones

The bones of the body fall into five general categories based on their shape.

1. **Long bones** are longer than they are wide and work as levers. The bones of the arms are of this type.
2. **Short bones** are short, cube-shaped, and found in the wrists and ankles.
3. **Flat bones** are not totally flat, but have broad smooth surfaces. Their function is primarily to protect organs and to attach muscles. Examples of these bones are the ribs, cranial bones and the scapulae.
4. **Sesamoid bones** are bones located within a tendon. An example is the patella. The person who named this type of bone gave it this name because they thought it looked like a sesame seed!
5. **Irregular bones** are all the bones that do not fall into the previous categories. They have varied shapes, sizes and surface features. This type of bone can be found in the vertebral column.

FIGURE 7.3 The structure of bone

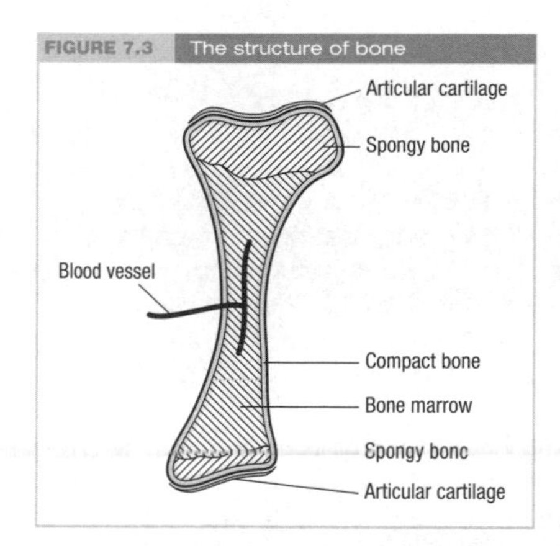

Structure of bone

Bones are composed of tissue that may take one of two forms: compact or spongy/cancellous. Most bones contain both types of tissue. **Compact** bone is dense, hard, and forms the protective external portion of all the bones. **Spongy** bone is inside the compact bone and is full of tiny holes filled with bone marrow. The spongy bone is usually found at the ends of the long bones.

Bone formation

The technical term for bone formation is **osteogenesis**. The process involves three main steps.

1. the production of an extracellular organic matrix
2. mineralization of the matrix to form bone
3. bone remodelling by resorption and reformation.

Osteoblasts, **osteocytes**, and **osteoclasts** are cells involved in the formation of bone. **Osteoblasts** start the process of bone formation by making collagen, which is the precursor of the extracellular matrix. Osteoblasts are also involved in laying down minerals in the matrix, supplied by the food a person eats. The minerals make the bone hard and able to withstand external forces. If a person has a diet lacking in calcium, they may suffer from a condition called osteoporosis, where the bones are weak and are more likely to break. As the process of bone formation progresses, the osteoblasts come to settle in the tiny spaces within the mineralized extracellular matrix of bone. Once the osteoblasts are positioned in the bone matrix, they are then called **osteocytes**.

Bone continually undergoes a process called **remodelling**. This involves bone reabsorption, where the bone is broken down by **osteoclasts** and then rebuilt by osteoblasts. This process allows us to grow, to repair broken bones and to build bigger, stronger bones in response to **weight bearing** exercise. Sunlight and/or Vitamin D are also necessary in order to ensure bone remodelling produces strong bones, as they help the process of laying down minerals in the bone.

STUDENT PRACTICAL

Bone measurements

Aim

The aim of this activity is to try to determine how the length of a person's bones contributes to their overall height and sporting potential.

Equipment

tape measure
pen and paper to record results

Method

Working in groups of three or four carry out the activity on the next page.

continues overleaf

continued

1 Draw up a table with the following columns: name, height, sport, humerus, radius and ulna, femur, tibia and fibula.
2 Write the names of the members of your group in the name column.
3 Record the height (in cm) of each member of your group.
4 Identify and write in the table the favourite sport of each member of your group.
5 With a tape measure, record in cm the length of the humerus of each person. Place the tape measure right at the top of the shoulder then measure down to the bony protrusions of the elbow. Write the length in the table.
6 Now measure the distance from the elbow down to the bony protrusions of the wrist. Record this distance in the radius and ulna column.
7 Feel for the top of the hip bone, then measure down the outside of the leg to the bony protrusions of the outside of the knee. Record this in the femur column.
8 From the knee joint, measure down to the outside of the lower leg to the bony protrusions of the ankle. Record this in the tibia and tibula column.
9 Compare your results with the rest of the group.

Conclusion

Try to answer the following questions.

1 What do you notice about the height of a person and the length of their limbs?
2 Is there a bone that is consistently the longest in each person? Which one is it?
3 Is there a relationship between a person's height and the type of sport they take part/compete in? Try to explain this relationship

STUDENT ACTIVITY

Bony features

Aim

The aim of this activity is to try to feel the bony features of the skeleton.

Equipment

Skeleton and selection of bones

Method

Students should work in pairs.

1 Run your fingers along different types of long, short, flat and irregular bones. Feel for bumps and dents on the surface of these bones. These bony features are called **protrusions** and **depressions** respectively.
2 Identify the following types of depressions.
a) A **fossa** – this is a rounded depression, e.g. the acetabular fossa located on the pelvis.
b) A **groove** – an elongated depression, e.g. the deep bicipital groove near to the head of the humerus which is occupied by one of the tendons of the biceps muscle.
c) A **notch** – a v-like depression, e.g. the sciatic notch on the pelvis.
3 Identify the following types of protrusions.
a) A **tuberosity** – this is a broad, rough, raised bump for muscle attachment, e.g. the tibial tuberosity.
b) A **tubercle** – this is a smaller version of the tuberosisty, e.g. the tubercle of the illiac crest.
c) A **spine** – this is a sharp pointed feature for muscle attachment, e.g. the iliac spine.
d) A **ridge**, **crest** or **line** – this is a moderately raised ridge along the shaft of a bone, e.g the tibial crest.
4 Protrusions that form part of a joint are called **condyles** and **epicondyles**.
a) Identify a **condyle** this is a rounded bump that usually fits into a fossa of another bone, thus making a joint.
b) Identify **epicondyle** this is a bump near a condyle and often gives the appearance of a bump on a bump.

Bone size

Aim

The aim of this activity is to try to determine if there is a difference in bone density and size between the different sexes, and between people from different ethnic origins.

Equipment

tape measure
paper
pen

Method

On a partner, measure the circumference of the bones at the wrist, elbow, ankle and knee. Ensure that you have measured the bony area of each body part.

Results

Make a results table with the headings shown:

Name	Wrist (cm)	Elbow (cm)	Ankle (cm)	Knee (cm)

Compare the class measurements.

Conclusion

In your conclusion try to answer the following questions.

1 Is there a difference between the measurements of the males and the females?
2 Is there an age-related difference in the measurements?
3 Try to explain the differences in circumference measurements.
4 Can you determine if there is a difference in bone density from these measurements?

FIGURE 7.4 The anatomical standing position

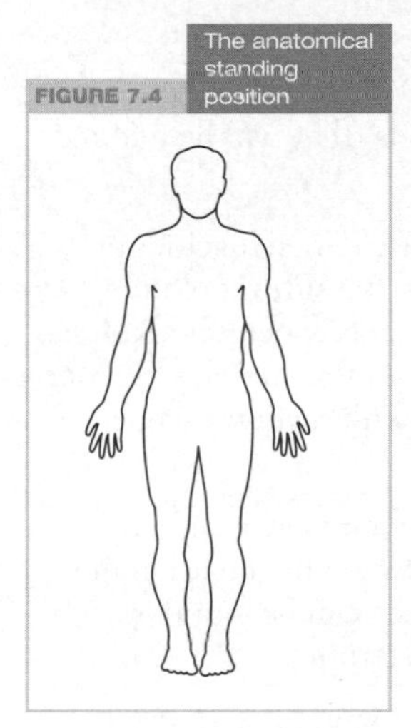

Anatomical language

Various terms are used to describe the body in anatomical positions and the position of structures related to each other. Correct anatomical terms must be used to express oneself clearly. All terms are related to the anatomical standing position of the human body, which is where the person stands with their feet hip

Terms of relationship

Copy out the list of names below and give an example of a body part that fits the description.

Anterior (ventral) – nearer the front of body, **e.g.** *the nose is on the* anterior *side of the body*

continues overleaf

Posterior (dorsal) – nearer the back surface of body, **e.g.**
Superior – towards the head or upper part of the body **e.g.**
Inferior – towards the feet or lower part of the body, **e.g.**
Medial – towards the midline or median plane of the body, **e.g.**
Lateral – away from the median plane of the body, **e.g.**

Terms of comparison

Proximal – nearest the trunk, **e.g.** *the humerus is proximal to the radius and ulna*
Distal – farthest from the trunk, **e.g.**
Superficial – nearer to the skin surface, **e.g.**
Deep – further from the skin surface, **e.g.**
Ipsilateral – on the same side of the body, **e.g.**
Contralateral – on the opposite side of the body, **e.g.**

JOINTS

distance apart, arms by the sides of their body and their palms facing forwards.

A joint is the place at which two or more bones meet, and can also be referred to as an **articulation**. The shape of a joint will determine how the bones can move in relation to each other. Some joints allow a lot of movement, while others allow no movement.

Types of joint

There are three classifications of joint which are based on the amount of movement they allow:

- **immoveable**, also know as **fibrous** joints
- **semi-moveable**, also known as **cartilaginous**
- **moveable**, more commonly called **synovial joints** (they will be referred to as such for the remainder of this chapter).

Immovable joints have no joint cavity and the bones are joined together by strong fibrous connective tissue. They can be found in the **sutures** of the cranium in the skull. At birth the skull has some 'soft spots' where the skull has not fused together. As a person grows, the skull sections grow in order to cover these soft spots. Where these skull sections join, immovable joints are formed.

FIGURE 7.5 Synovial joint

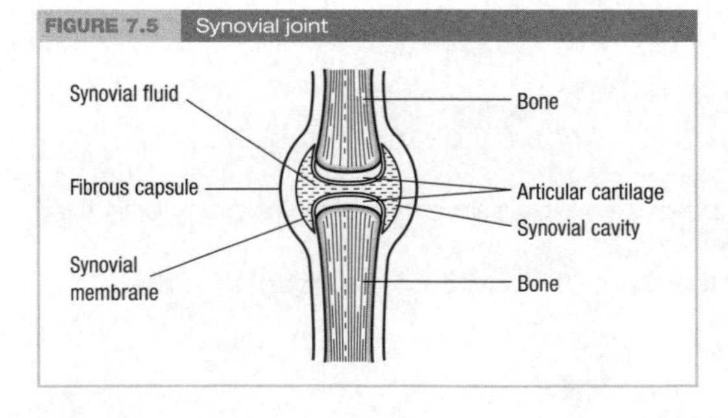

Semi-moveable joints have no joint cavity either, however, there is cartilage between the bones in the joint. An example of where they can be found is between the clavical and the sternum.

Synovial joints allow the greatest range of movement because they contain synovial fluid and have a joint cavity (see Figure 7.5).

FIGURE 7.6 Gliding joint

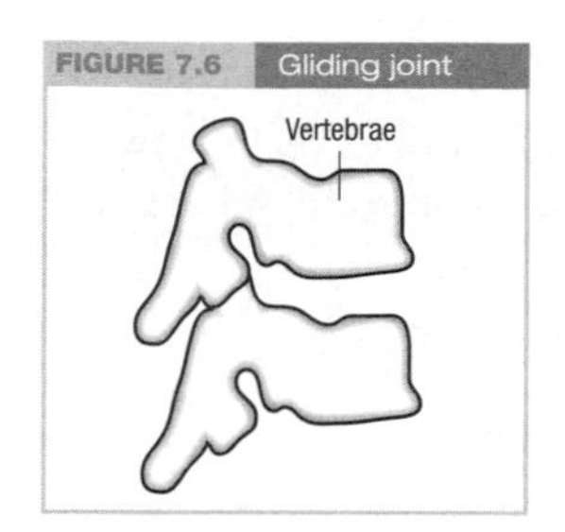

Synovial joints

There are six types of synovial joint. The shape of the joint will determine how much movement is allowed – some synovial joints have a very wide range of movement, whereas others allow comparatively little.

Gliding

This type of joint allows one bone to slide over another (see Figure 7.6). This type of joint is present between the vertebrae. The movement between the two surfaces is extremely small. The joints between the carpals and tarsals are also gliding joints.

FIGURE 7.7 Hinge joint

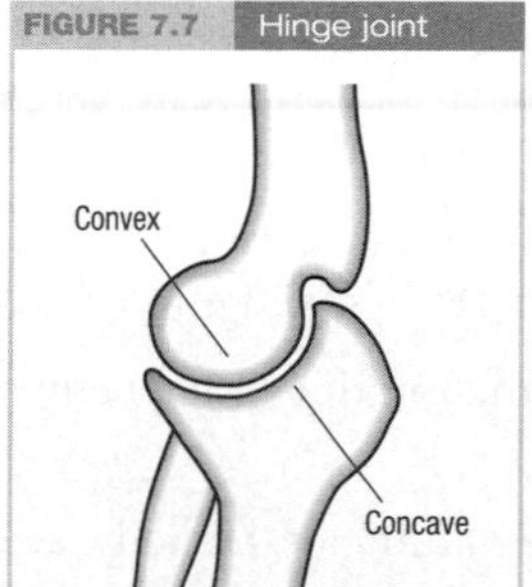
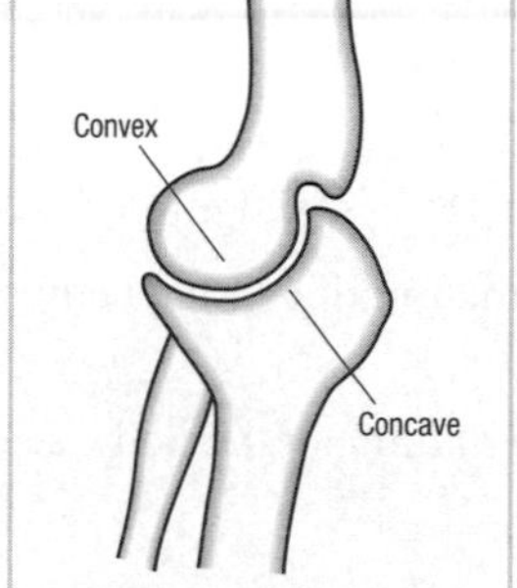

Hinge

This joint is so named because it allows movement like that of a hinge (see Figure 7.7). It has one **convex** surface, which fits into another **concave** surface. It allows movement in one plane about a single axis, just like the hinge of a door. The types of movement it allows are called flexion and extension. The elbow joint is an example of this type of joint.

Ball and socket

FIGURE 7.8 Ball and socket joint

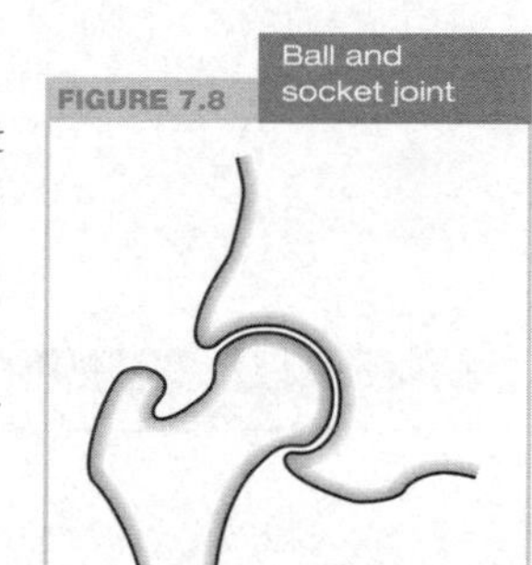

This type of joint allows the greatest range of movement of all the synovial joints as it has the capacity to move in three planes, about three axes (see Figure 7.8). The actions of flexion, extension, inward and outward rotation, abduction, adduction and circumduction are all possible with this type of joint. The hip and shoulder joints are examples of a ball and socket joint.

FIGURE 7.9 Condyloid

Condyloid

This joint is also known as an **ellipsoidal** joint (see Figure 7.9). It is similar to the ball and socket joint, except that movement can occur in only two planes, forward and backward (flexion and extension), and from side to side (abduction and adduction). The wrist is an example of this type of joint.

FIGURE 7.10 Pivot joint

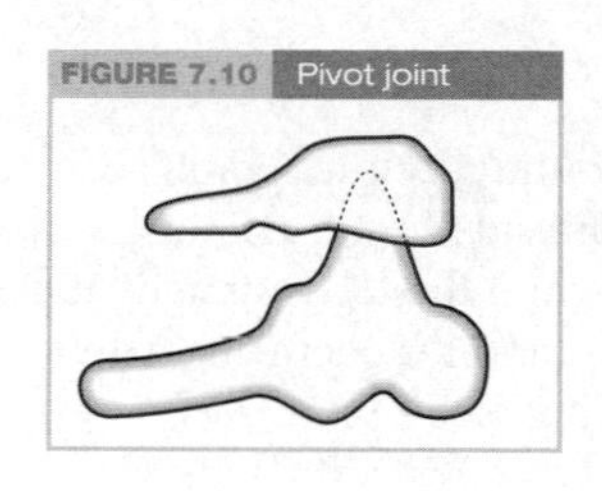

Pivot

This joint allows rotation, which is a movement in one plane about one axis (see Figure 7.10). An example of this joint can be found between the atlas and the axis of the neck.

Saddle

This joint allows movement principally in one plane, about one axis (see Figure 7.11). A limited amount of rotation and sliding can also occur. The thumb is an example of a saddle joint.

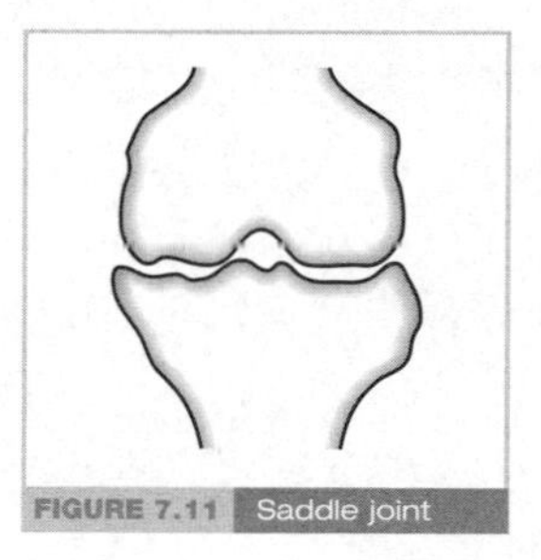

FIGURE 7.11 Saddle joint

Types of movement

Ways in which joints move have technical names which will be described. Remember, when you are describing a type of movement, always refer to the joint that is moving. For example, when a person is kicking a ball you would say that the knee joint was flexing rather than the leg was flexing, because the leg consists of three joints – the hip, the knee and the ankle.

Joint movements are generally divided into four types: gliding, angular, rotation and circumduction.

Gliding

Gliding is the simplest type of motion. It is basically one surface moving over another without any rotary or angular motion. This type of movement occurs between two adjacent surfaces.

Angular

Angular motion decreases or increases the angle between two adjoining bones. The more common types of angular motion are as follows. (See also pages 388–89.)

FIGURE 7.12 Flexion

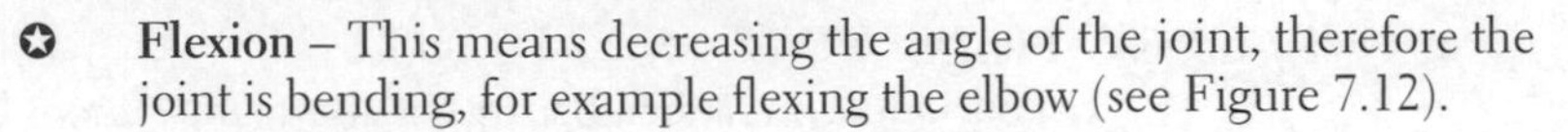

- **Flexion** – This means decreasing the angle of the joint, therefore the joint is bending, for example flexing the elbow (see Figure 7.12).

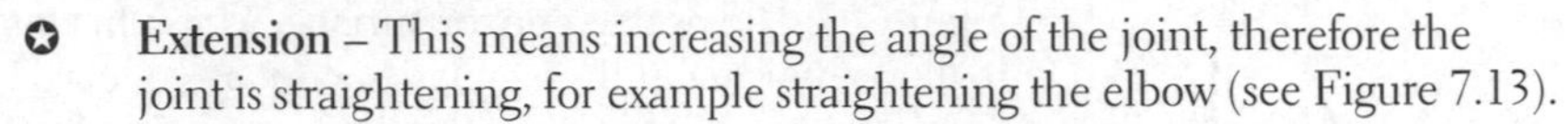

- **Extension** – This means increasing the angle of the joint, therefore the joint is straightening, for example straightening the elbow (see Figure 7.13).

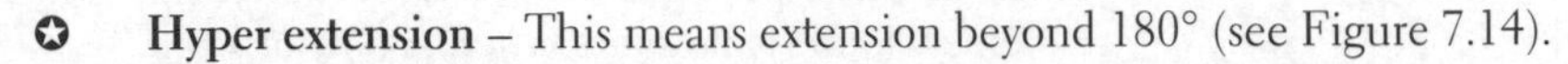

- **Hyper extension** – This means extension beyond 180° (see Figure 7.14).

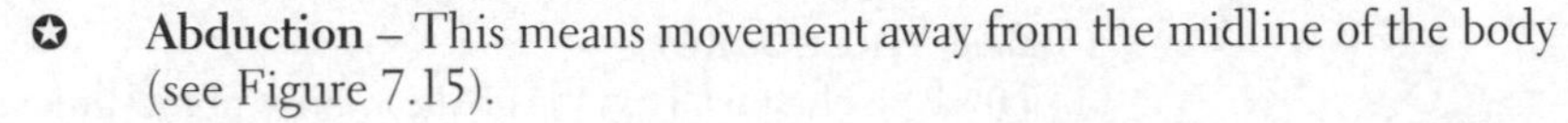

- **Abduction** – This means movement away from the midline of the body (see Figure 7.15).
- **Adduction** – This means movement towards the midline of the body (see Figure 7.16).

FIGURE 7.13 Extension

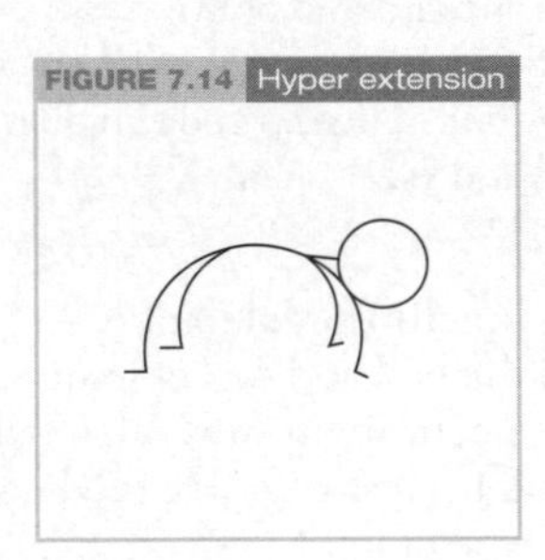

FIGURE 7.14 Hyper extension

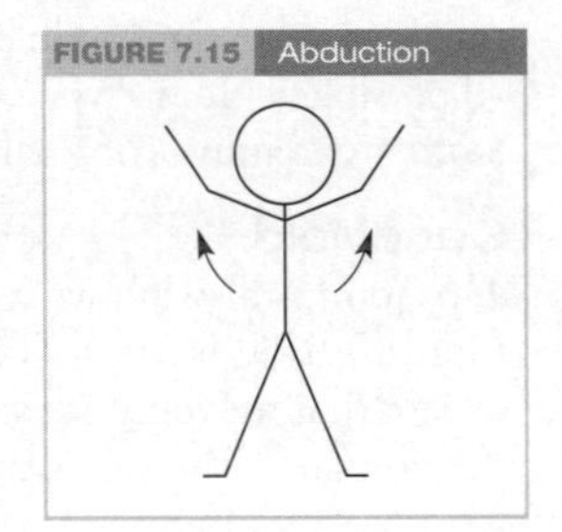

FIGURE 7.15 Abduction

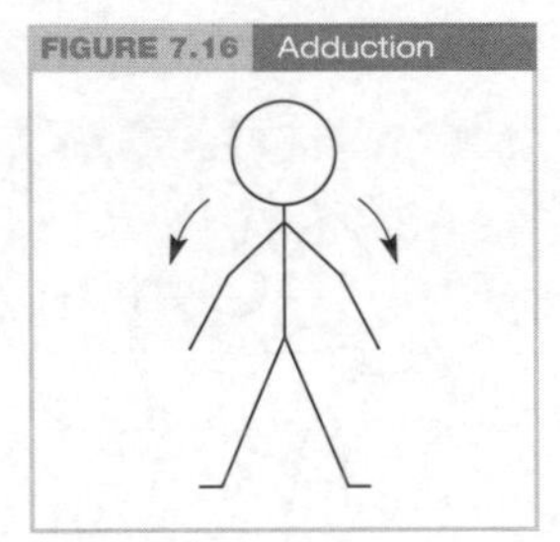

FIGURE 7.16 Adduction

Rotation

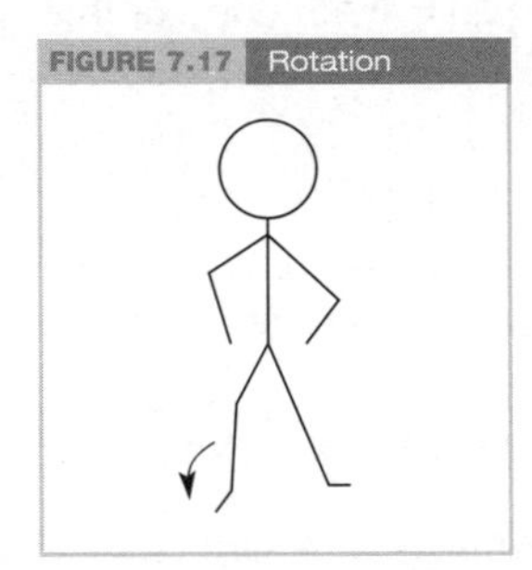

FIGURE 7.17 Rotation

Rotation is a movement in which the bone moves around a central point without being displaced, such as turning the head from side to side. Both internal and external rotation can occur. At the hip, when the leg is straight and turned so that the foot turns in to the body, internal rotation is occurring; when the leg is turned outwards, external rotation is occurring (see Figure 7.17).

Circumduction

FIGURE 7.18 Circumduction

Circumduction involves a combination of flexion, extension, abduction and adduction. This type of action can only occur at ball and socket joints at the shoulder and the hip (see Figure 7.18).

Other types of movement

Other types of movement generally used to indicate movement at specific anatomical positions include the following. (See also page 389.)

- **Supination** – Turning upwards, as in turning the palm of the hand upwards.
- **Pronation** – Turning downwards, as in turning the palm of the hand downwards.
- **Eversion** – Turning outwards, as in turning the sole of the foot to the outside.
- **Inversion** – Turning inwards, as in turning the sole of the foot inwards.
- **Plantar flexion** – This only occurs at the ankle joint, and involves pointing the foot downwards.
- **Dorsi flexion** – This only occurs at the ankle joint, and involves bringing the foot up towards the shin.
- **Elevation** – Moving the shoulders upwards.
- **Depression** – Moving the shoulders downwards.

Devise an aerobic/dance routine that includes the following movements in their correct order. You decide which joint carries out the movement. Write down the routine as you go and make a note of each joint you will be moving. You may repeat each movement as many times as you wish and must also be prepared to repeat your whole routine at least three times. You could use music to accompany your routine if the equipment is available.

1 Circumduction
2 Flexion
3 Extention
4 Plantar flexion
5 Dorsi flexion
6 Hyperextension
7 Abduction
8 Adduction

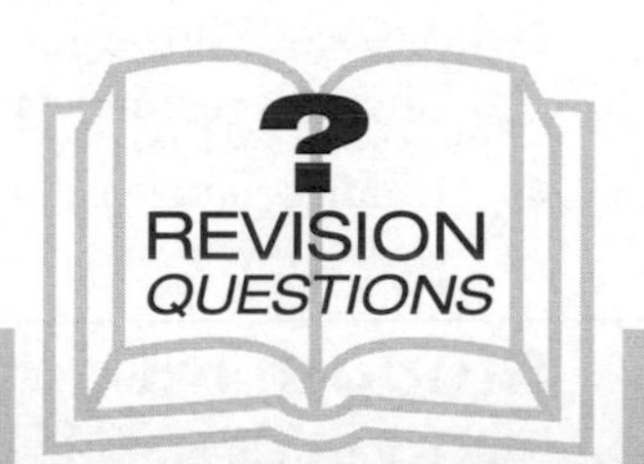

1) What are the functions of the skeleton?
2) The skeleton is split into two main sections, the axial and the appendicular. Name the bones of each.
3) Where would you find spongy bone?
4) Explain how bone is formed.
5) What are the different classifications of bone? Give an example of each type.
6) Draw a diagram of a synovial joint.
7) How many different types of joint are there? Give an example of where you would find each in the body.

MUSCLE

Humans use muscles in order to produce movement. Muscles produce this movement by converting the chemical energy of ATP into mechanical work. Three different kinds of muscles are found in humans:

- cardiac muscle
- smooth muscle
- skeletal muscle.

Both **cardiac** and **smooth** muscle are also known as **involuntary** muscle, which means we do not have to think about moving them. **Skeletal** muscles are also known as **voluntary** muscles as they are under our conscious control – in order to move them we have to think about moving them. This means that we can think, 'I want to throw this ball', and our skeletal muscles move in order for us to carry out this movement.

Cardiac muscle

Cardiac muscle, as its name implies, is only found in the heart. It makes up the wall of the heart. It has a striped appearance under the microscope.

Throughout life, the heart is constantly contracting and then briefly relaxing. If the heart stops contracting the person dies. An adult's heart beats around 70 times per minute and pumps about 5 litres of blood each minute. Cardiac muscle has a number of unique features:

- it does not **fatigue**
- all parts of the cardiac muscle contract in a synchronous wave because the cells are interconnected
- cardiac muscle can generate its own nervous impulses; this is known as being **myogenic**.

Smooth muscle

This is found in the walls of all the hollow organs of the body (except the heart). It contracts in order to reduce the size of these organs. Examples of where it is found and what it does are as follows:

- regulates the flow of blood in the arteries
- moves food through the **gastrointestinal tract**
- expels urine from the bladder
- regulates the flow of air through the lungs.

Smooth muscle is made of single, spindle-shaped cells. It gets its name because no striations (stripes) are visible in them.

Smooth muscle is entirely dependent on aerobic respiration, and therefore has many **mitochondria**. Smooth muscles do not contract as rapidly as skeletal muscle, but the contraction can be for a much longer time than contractions of skeletal muscles.

Skeletal muscle

As the name implies, skeletal muscle is attached to the skeleton. It is also called **striated muscle** because of its striated (striped) appearance under the microscope.

The primary function of skeletal muscle is locomotion and posture. The skeletal muscles are the longest of the three types and are controlled voluntarily. Skeletal muscle is called voluntary muscle because it is the only type that can be

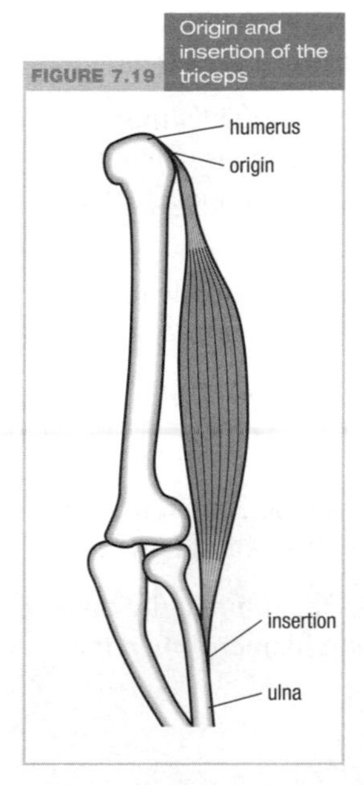

FIGURE 7.19 Origin and insertion of the triceps

consciously controlled. Skeletal muscle fibres are **multi-nucleate**, meaning that each muscle cell has many nuclei. Also, because of their tremendous demand for energy, muscle cells have a high concentration of enzymes and mitochondria which are necessary for the production of energy (ATP).

Skeletal muscles can contract rapidly and can exert tremendous amounts of force, but they tire quickly and have to rest after periods of activity.

Structure of skeletal muscle

Attachment to the skeleton

Muscles are attached to the skeleton in two places by tendons. The **origin** of the muscle is where the muscle is attached to a large area of bone – this is the part of the muscle that tends not to move during muscle contraction. At its other end is the **insertion**. Taking the triceps as an example, the origin is at the humerus and the insertion is on the ulna (see Figure 7.19).

As the triceps contracts, the insertion is pulled toward the origin and the arm is straightened or extended at the elbow.

Gross muscle structure

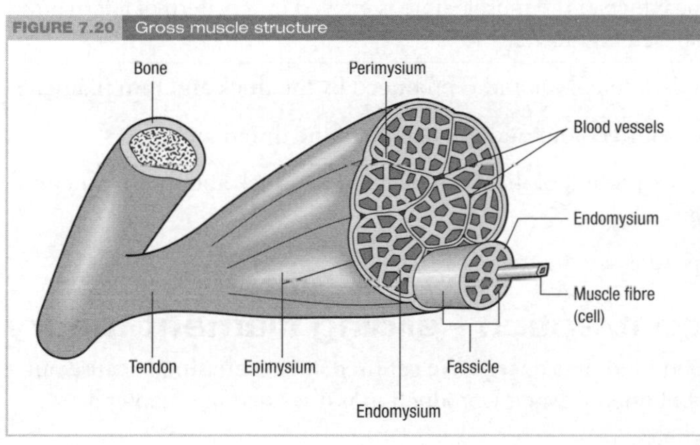

FIGURE 7.20 Gross muscle structure

- **Tendons** – These are made up of collagen and attach muscle to bone.
- **Epimysium** – This is the outer layer of the muscle, which is made up of dense connective tissue.
- **Fassicle** – A fassicle is a collection of muscle fibres that lies under the epimysium. Inside each fassicle there are many muscle fibres.
- **Perimysium** – The perimysium is a fibrous tissue that covers each fassicle and is made up of collagen fibres.
- **Muscle fibres** – Inside each fassicle, there are many muscle fibres. The muscle fibre is the place where contraction occurs. The separate muscle fibres are held together by endomysium. Each muscle fibre consists of many contractile units called myofibrils.
- **Endomysium** – Each muscle fibre is surrounded by endomysium, which holds the fibres together.

Cellular structure of muscle fibres

The muscle fibre is composed of smaller microscopic elements (see Figure 7.21).

- **Sarcolemma** – The sarcolemma is the correct term for the cell membrane of the muscle cell. Its functions are exactly the same as the functions of a typical cell membrane.

FIGURE 7.21 Cellular structure of muscle fibres

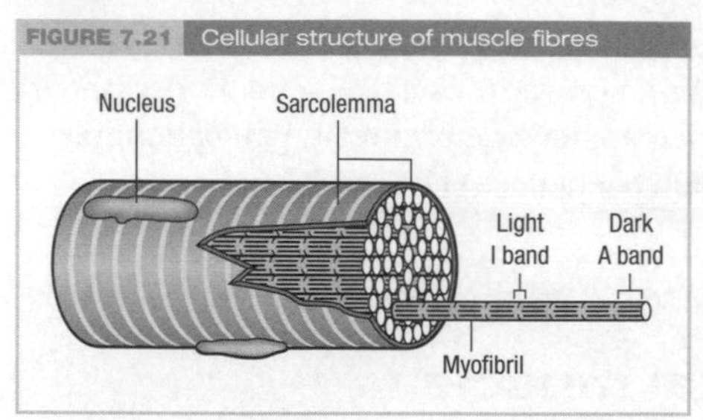

- **Myofibrils** – The myofibrils contain the small, contracting units of the muscle called the sarcomeres.
- **Sarcoplasm** – The sarcoplasm is essentially the same as the **cytoplasm** of a normal cell. It contains all of the usual cell organelles and some that are specific to the muscle cells.
- **Sarcoplasmic reticulum** – This is essentially the same as **endoplasmic reticulum**, which is present in all cells.
- **Sarcomere** – This is the smallest functional part of the skeletal muscle.
- **Actin** – This is the thin filament involved in muscle contraction.
- **Myosin** – This is the thick filament involved in muscle contraction. It is called thick because it has 'heads' that attach it to the actin filament.
- **Troponin and tropomyosin** – These are proteins that bind to the myosin filament and prevent it from attaching to the actin filament when the muscles are at rest.

The anatomy of a sarcomere

FIGURE 7.22 Bands of muscle fibre

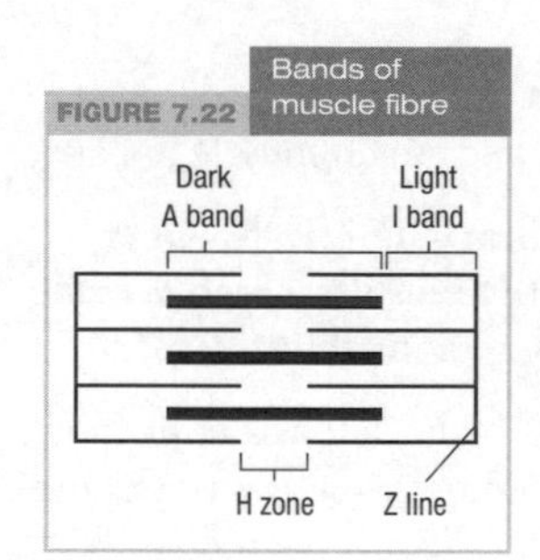

The striated appearance of the muscle fibre is created by a pattern of alternating bands of material (see Figure 7.22).

- **A band** is dark in colour and is produced by the thick and thin filaments
- **I band** is light in colour and is made up of the thin filaments
- **H zone** is the portion of the A band where the thick and thin filaments do not overlap
- **Z line** separates sarcomeres.

Muscle contraction – sliding filament theory

Muscle contraction requires energy. We get tired after exercising because our muscles run out of energy. Energy production is discussed in Chapter 4 Exercise Physiology.

So how does energy enable our muscles to contract? The contraction process occurs in four steps.

1. At rest, troponin and tropomyosin cover the actin and myosin filaments and prevent myosin from binding to actin. When we give the signal for our muscles to contract, calcium is released into the sarcoplasm. Calcium binds to troponin and takes it away from the myosin binding site. As it moves away, it moves the tropomyosin molecule with it. Therefore, as the troponin and tropomyosin bind to calcium, the myosin binding site is exposed.
2. The mysoin heads bind to the actin filament and slide it across the myosin filament, which results in the sarcomere getting shorter.

3. Energy is used to break the attachment of the actin and myosin filaments. The myosin heads then re-attach at a site further up the actin filament which results in further shortening of the sarcomere.
4. When the stimulus to the muscle ends, calcium ions are released from the troponin and are pumped out of the sarcoplsam. This causes the troponin and tropomyosin to bind to the myosin heads once again, which means they cannot bind to the actin molecule, and contraction cannot occur.

The entire process is extremely fast and only takes a fraction of a second. The cycle then repeats itself until the muscle relaxes.

Why dead people are called 'stiffs'

When a person dies, their body becomes very rigid and stiff. This process is called rigor mortis. The muscles begin to stiffen three to four hours after the time of death and the stiffness will usually last 48 to 60 hours. Studying rigor mortis can help to determine the time of death in murder cases.

The reason rigor mortis occurs is because there is a high level of calcium ions inside the muscle, which enables the actin and myosin filaments to bind together. As there is no longer any energy production to break the bond between the actin and myosin filaments, the myosin heads cannot release from the actin fibres, so the muscle remains contracted and stiff.

Muscle fibre types

Not all skeletal muscle fibres are alike in structure or function: they vary in colour, contract with different velocities, fatigue at different rates and vary with respect to the metabolic processes they use to generate ATP. Therefore, based on the various structural and functional characteristics, skeletal muscle fibres are classified into three types (see Table 7.1, overleaf).

1. **Type I fibres** – These fibres, also called **slow twitch** or **slow oxidative** fibres, and are a red colour because they contain large amounts of **myoglobin**. They also contain many mitochondria and many blood capillaries. As they split ATP at a slow rate, they have a slow contraction speed. They are very resistant to fatigue and have a high capacity to generate ATP by oxidative metabolic processes. Such fibres are found in large numbers in the legs of world-class endurance runners.
2. **Type II A fibres** – These fibres are also called **fast twitch** or **fast oxidative** fibres. They are very similar to type 1 fibres as they are also red in colour, contain very large amounts of myoglobin, many mitochondria and many blood capillaries. They also have a very high capacity for generating ATP by oxidative metabolic processes and are resistant to fatigue. However, these fibres differ from type I fibres because they split ATP at a very rapid rate and have a fast contraction speed.
3. **Type II B fibres** – These fibres are also called **fast twitch** or **fast glycolytic** fibres. They are white in colour because they contain a low content of myoglobin, relatively few mitochondria, few blood capillaries

and large amounts glycogen. They generate ATP by anaerobic metabolic processes, fatigue easily, split ATP at a fast rate and have a fast contraction speed. Such fibres are found in large numbers in the leg muscles of world-class sprinters.

From the list of sports people below, state which fibre type dominates in their arms and legs. Explain your decisions.

Steve Redgrave
David Beckham
Denise Lewis
Paula Radcliff
Lennox Lewis
Ian Thorpe
Tiger Woods
Venus Williams

Table 7.1 Characteristics of muscle fibre types

Characteristic	Type 1 fibres	Type II A fibres	Type II B fibres
Contraction speed	Slow	Fast	Very fast
Colour	Red	Red	White
Resistance to fatigue	High	Intermediate	Low
Force production	Low	High	Very high
Capillary density	High	Intermediate	Low
Mitochondria	Lots	Lots	Few
Energy system	Aerobic	Aerobic and anaerobic	Anaerobic

Most skeletal muscle is a mixture of all three types of skeletal muscle fibres. However, the proportion of the muscle fibres in each muscle varies in relation to the usual action of the muscle. For example, postural muscles of the neck, back and leg have a higher proportion of type I fibres as they are almost constantly being used.

Effects of exercise on muscle fibre type

Research to date suggests that it is not possible to change the proportion of muscle fibre types within your muscle tissue. Therefore, the proportion of the different types of muscle fibre you have in your body is determined by your parents' genes. So, if a child has two parents who are world-class sprinters, it would be assumed that they have a very high proportion of fast twitch muscles in their legs. Their child would then inherit these fast twitch muscles in their legs and therefore also have the potential to be a very good sprinter.

However, despite the fact that it appears you are born with a certain proportion of fast and slow twitch muscles in your body, which cannot be altered, it is possible to change the **characteristics** of some muscle fibre types. Endurance exercises, such as running long distances or swimming long distances, can gradually transform type II B fibres into type II A fibres. Prolonged endurance training has been shown to increase the diameter of type II B fibres, increase the number of mitochondria in the muscle fibres and increase the number of blood capillaries surrounding the muscle fibre. All these changes enable the muscle fibre to use the aerobic energy system more efficiently because there is an increased supply of oxygen to the muscle tissue. Strength training has an effect on the type II B fibres by increasing the size of the fibres. The number of muscle fibres will remain the same, but because the size of the muscle fibres is increased, the athlete will have a greater muscle mass which will make them stronger.

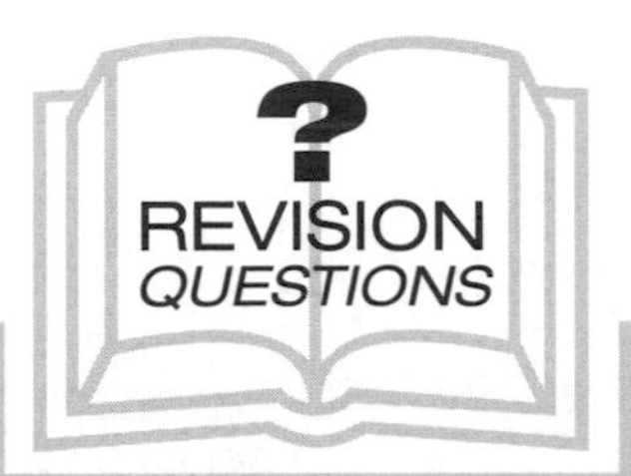

1) What are the differences between the different types of muscle tissue?
2) Give examples in the body where you would find each of the different types of muscle tissue.
3) What does myogenic mean?
4) Draw and label a diagram of skeletal muscle. Include in your drawing the following structures:
- epimysium
- perimysium
- fassicle
- endomysium
- muscle fibres
- sarcomere.

5) Explain the processes involved in a muscle contraction.
6) Name the different muscle fibre types and give the characteristics of each.
7) Explain how endurance training affects muscle fibre types.
8) Why is it said that you have to be 'born a sprinter' rather than becoming one through training?
9) How does weight training increase a person's strength?

SKELETAL AND NEURO-MUSCULAR SYSTEMS

Muscle

FIGURE 7.23 Anterior superficial muscles of the body

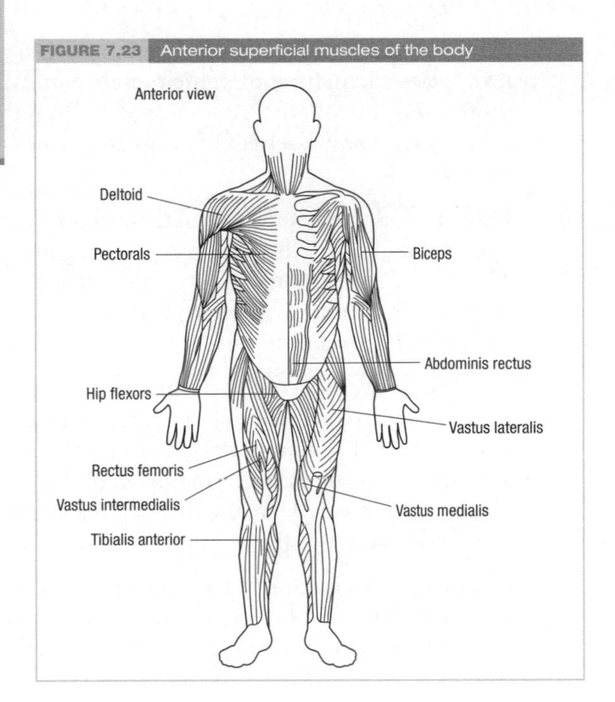

FIGURE 7.24 Posterior superficial muscles of the body

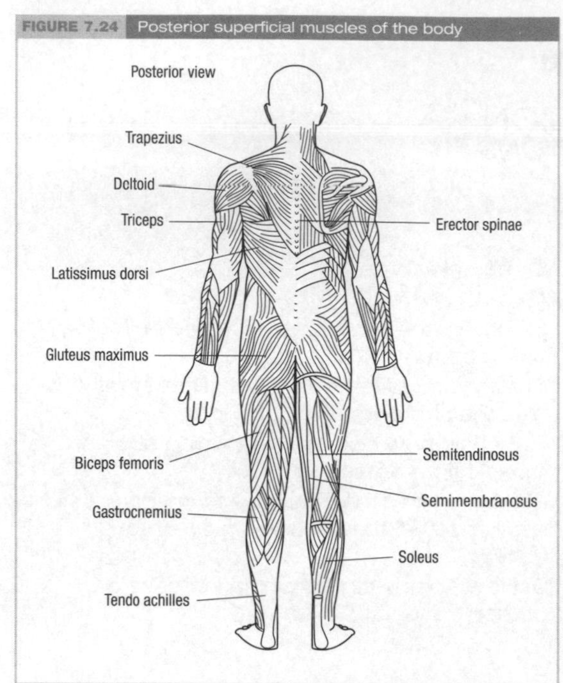

Working in pairs, copy down the list of muscles below on to separate sticky labels.

gastrocnemius	erector spinae
deltoids	biceps femoris
pectorals	tibialis anterior
biceps	gluteus maximus
soleus	abdomis rectus
latissimus dorsi	trapezius

One of you is to be the 'model'. Place each sticky label on top of the model's clothing under which lies the named muscle. Once you have completed the activity, check with Figures 7.23 and 7.24 to ensure you have placed all the labels in the correct places.

Types of contraction

There are four main types of muscle contraction. (See also page 387–88.)

1. **Concentric** – This is the most common type of muscle contraction. It takes place when the ends of the muscle come closer together so the muscle is getting shorter. An example of this is the hamstrings (semimembranosus, semitendinosus and biceps femoris) contracting and flexing the knee.
2. **Eccentric** – An eccentric contraction occurs when the muscle is exerting a force but the ends of the muscle are moving further away from each other. This type of contraction usually occurs when a muscle is exerting a braking type of force in order to control a body part. An example of this is the biceps working eccentrically during the lowering phase of a biceps curl.
3. **Isometric** – An isometric contraction is where the muscle is exerting a force but there is no movement of the body part and no change in length of the muscle. If you push down hard on to your desk with your hand, you are still creating tension in your arm muscles but no movement is taking place (unless the desk breaks, that is!). A sporting example of this would be a tug of war when there is no movement of the rope.
4. **Isokinetic** – An isokinetic contraction occurs when the muscle is producing a tension but is working at a constant speed. This type of contraction can only occur if specialised weight-training equipment is used.

STUDENT ACTIVITY

Muscle contractions

Wearing appropriate clothing and with appropriate equipment if available, carry out the following activities:

- a press up
- a sit up
- an arm wrestle
- a ski squat.

For each exercise, analyse one muscle and complete and extend the table below for each exercise.

Activity	Phase	Muscle	Type of contraction
Press up	Downwards phase	Triceps	
Press up	Upwards phase	Triceps	

Function of muscles

Muscles work in pairs; as one muscle contracts the other relaxes. Muscles that work together are called **antagonistic pairs** (see also pages 389–90). Muscles have to work in pairs because a muscle can only pull on a bone, it cannot push the bone back to its original position – the other muscle is responsible for this. A good example of this pairing is the biceps and triceps (see Figure 7.25). As the biceps contract, the triceps relax and the elbow joint is flexed. To straighten the arm, the biceps relax and the triceps contract.

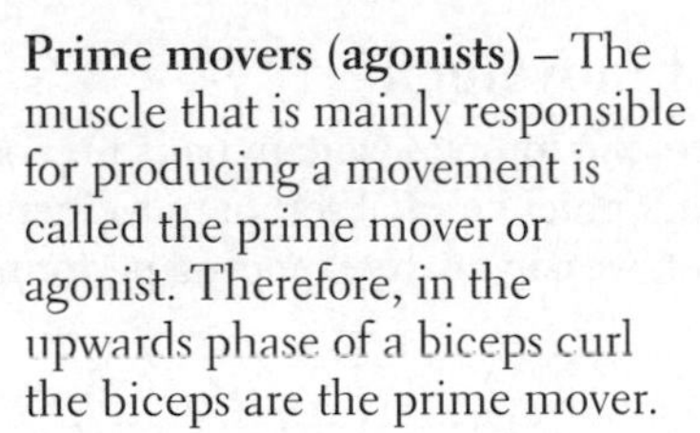

STUDENT ACTIVITY

Work out which muscles are paired with the muscles below.
hamstrings
gastrocnemius
latissimus dorsi
abdominals
pectorals
deltoids
gluteals
abductors

Prime movers (agonists) – The muscle that is mainly responsible for producing a movement is called the prime mover or agonist. Therefore, in the upwards phase of a biceps curl the biceps are the prime mover.

Antagonist – These muscles pull in the opposite to the direction to that of the agonist. When the movement by the prime mover is completed, the antagonist contracts and returns the part moved to its original position. An example of this is the triceps during the downwards phase of a biceps curl.

FIGURE 7.25 The biceps and triceps work as an antagonistic pair

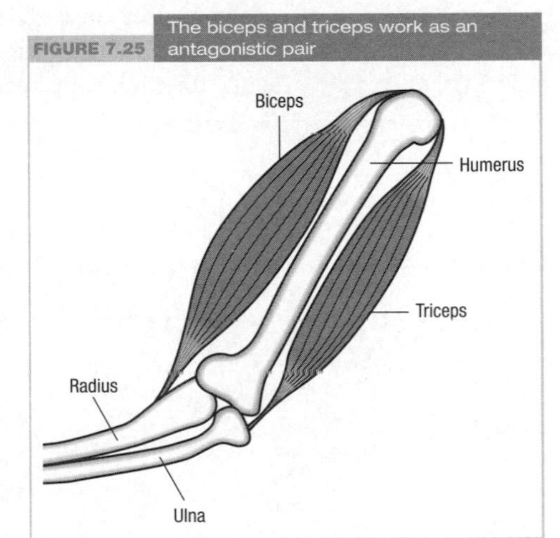

Synergist – A synergist acts to 'help' the prime mover. It produces an additional force in the same general direction as the prime mover.

Stabilizer – A stabilizer muscle ensures that the joint being moved is properly maintained.

Fixator – A fixator acts to keep the other joints of the body still when one joint is being moved.

Table 7.2 Muscle groups and their actions

Muscle group	Origin	Insertion	Joint	Action
Biceps	Shoulder and scapula	Radius	Elbow	Flexion
Triceps	Humerus and scapula	Ulna	Elbow	Extension
Deltoids	Scapula and clavicle	Humerus	Shoulder	Abduction
Latissimus Dorsi	Spine	Scapula	Shoulder	Adduction
Abdominals	Pubis	Ribs	Spine	Flexion
Erector Spinae	Ribs and illium	Spine and ribs	Spine	Extension
Gastrocnemius	Femur	Calcaneous (heel)	Ankle	Plantar flexion
Tibialis anterior	Tibia	Ankle	Ankle	Dorsi flexion
Hip flexors	Spine and hips	Femur	Hip	Hip flexion
Gluteals	Illium and sacrum	Femur	Hip	Hip extension
Quadriceps	Illium	Patella and tibia	Knee	Extension
Hamstrings	Ischium	Tibia	Knee	Flexion
Abductors	Illium	Femur	Hip	Abduction
Adductors	Pubic bone	Femur	Hip	Adduction
Pectorals	Clavicle and sternum	Top of humerus	Shoulder	Rotation and shoulder

Production of movement

As previously stated, the muscles work in pairs to produce movement. Now we know which muscles produce what sort of movements, and the technical term for each movement, we can analyse sporting performance.

A biceps curl

Study these drawings.

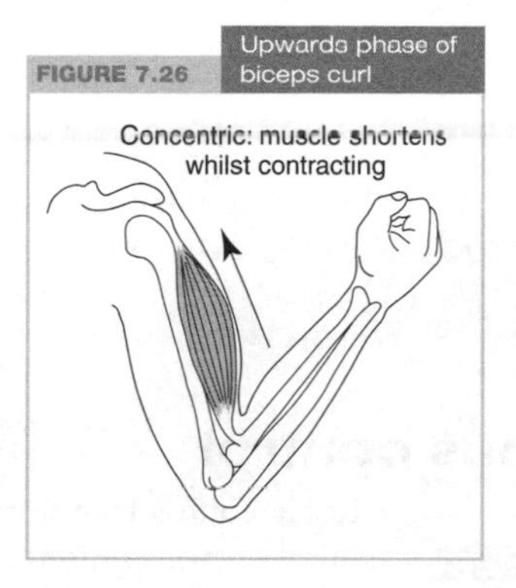

FIGURE 7.26 Upwards phase of biceps curl

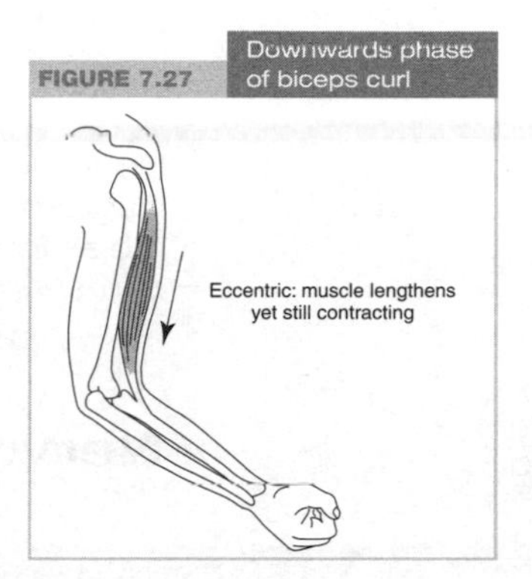

FIGURE 7.27 Downwards phase of biceps curl

Now study the table below.

Sport movement	Joint	Type of movement	Agonist	Antagonist
Biceps curl – upwards phase	Elbow	Flexion	Biceps	Triceps
Biceps curl – Downwards phase	Elbow	Extension	Triceps	Biceps

A football kick

Study these drawings.

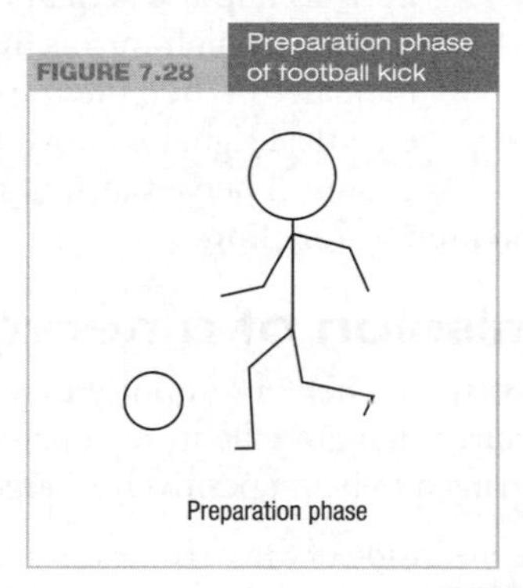

FIGURE 7.28 Preparation phase of football kick

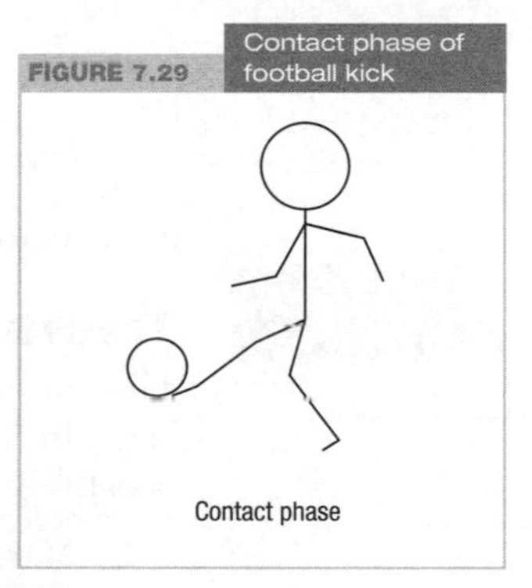

FIGURE 7.29 Contact phase of football kick

continues overleaf

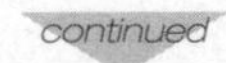

Now copy and complete the table below.

Sport movement	Joint	Type of movement	Agonist	Antagonist
Football kick – phase 1	Knee Hip	Flexion	 Gluteals	Quadriceps
Football kick – phase 2	Knee Hip	Extension	 Hip flexors	Hamstrings

Now choose three sporting actions with two phases. Draw a stick man diagram to show the movement you are going to analyse, then complete tables for each, ensuring that you analyse at least two joints in each type of movement.

Nervous control

FIGURE 7.30 A neurone or nerve cell

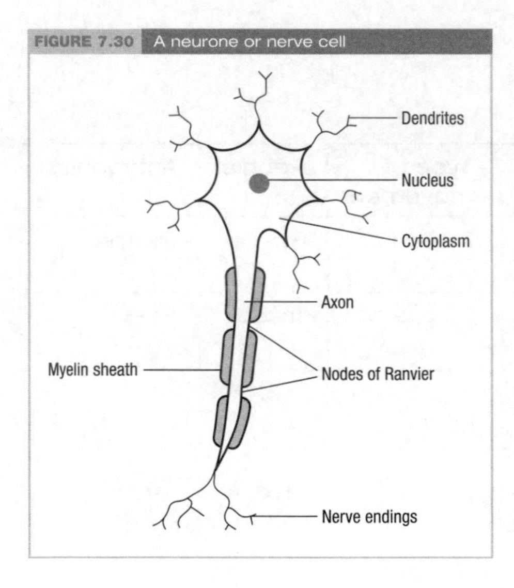

Muscle contracts in response to stimulation from nerves. The central nervous system (CNS) includes the brain and spinal cord and is responsible for stimulating the nervous system to carry an electrical impulse to the required muscle in order to produce movement. The nervous impulse is carried through **neurones** or nerve cells (see Figure 7.30). Some neurones stretch all the way from the CNS to the muscle, whereas others are shorter and connect to other neurones in order to transmit the stimulation to the correct muscle group. The connection between two neurones is called a **synapse**.

The nervous impulse travels down the axon, which is covered in a myelin sheath. The thicker the myelin sheath, the faster the nerve impulse will travel. The myelin sheath has gaps in it which are called 'Nodes of Ranvier'. The nervous impulse actually jumps from one Node of Ranvier to the next, which means that the speed of the impulse is increased. When the impulse reaches the axon terminal the electrical signal is converted to a chemical signal, as a chemical nerve transmitter called acetylecholine is released at the **neuromuscular junction**.

FIGURE 7.31 An axon at resting potential

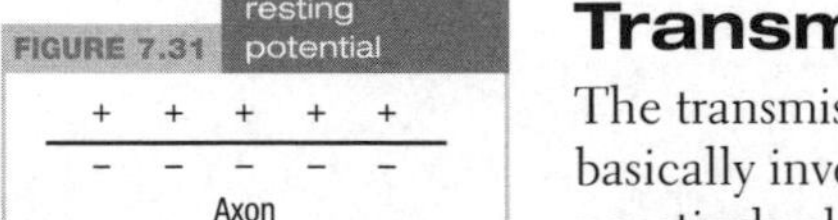

Transmission of a nervous impulse

The transmission of a nervous impulse is quite a complicated procedure, but it basically involves changing the inside of a nerve cell's axon from being negatively charged to being positively charged.

1 At rest, the inside of the nerve axon is negatively charged and the outside is positively charged (see Figure 7.31). This is called the **resting potential**.

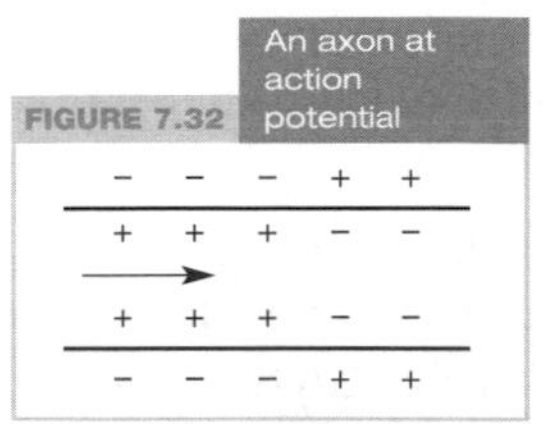
FIGURE 7.32 An axon at action potential

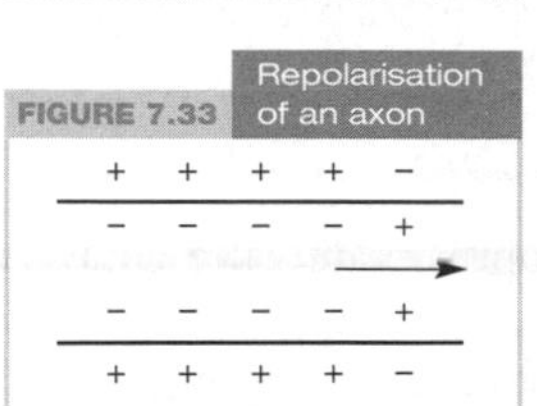
FIGURE 7.33 Repolarisation of an axon

2. When the CNS stimulates a nerve, the inside of the axon becomes positively charged and the outside becomes negatively charged (see Figure 7.32). This change is called the **action potential**.
3. When the CNS stops stimulating the nerve, the axon returns to its resting state, where the inside of the axon is negatively charged and the outside is positively charged (see Figure 7.33). This process is called **repolarisation**.

Reflex

Reflexes are used to protect the body without having to think about what is happening, e.g. if a person puts their hand on a hot stove they will immediately remove their hand without having to think about it.

The knee jerk is a well-known reflex. It is called a **monosynaptic** reflex, which means there is only one synapse in the circuit. The movement it produces takes place very quickly because there is only one synapse. The reflex works by tapping just below the knee, which makes the quadriceps muscle stretch. This information travels to the spinal cord. There, after one synapse in the spinal cord, the information is sent back out to the muscle, which makes it contract, and the knee extends.

Reflex tests

There are a range of other reflexes that can be demonstrated by carrying out the following activities. Work in pairs for these activities.

1) One person should sit on a chair with their legs crossed. The other person should then tap the first person's top leg just below the knee.
2) For this activity, make sure you are in a well-lit room. Close your eyes and place your hand over your eyes for one minute. Your partner should then observe the size of your pupils when you open your eyes, and see what happens to them over the following few seconds.
3) Gently stroke the outer edges of the soles of your partner's feet with the blunt end of a pen or ruler. Check to see if their big toe extends out as a result. This is called the Babinski reflex.
4) Carry out some research to find an example of another reflex.

The muscle spindle

The knee jerk reflex works because of muscle spindles located within the muscles. The purpose of muscle spindles is to record the change in length of a muscle and transmit this information to the spine (see Figure 7.30).

FIGURE 7.34 A muscle spindle

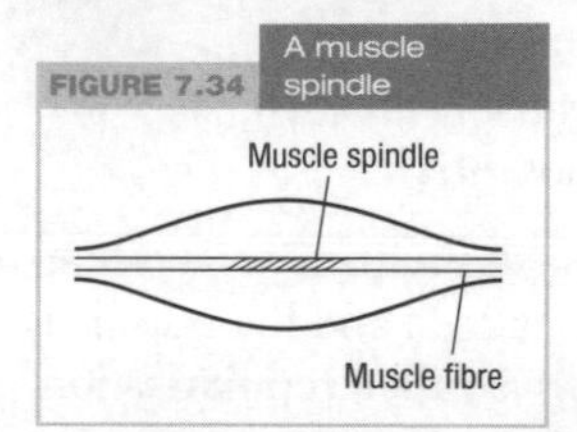

This will then make the muscle attempt to resist this change in length by contracting the stretched muscle. The quicker the change in muscle length, the stronger the muscle contractions will be.

Therefore, the muscle spindle helps to maintain muscle tone and helps to protect the body from injury. Flexibility training is based on training the muscle spindle to become used to an increased length of muscle. Therefore, stretches should be held for a period of time so that the muscle spindles will eventually allow greater lengthening of the muscles.

THE CARDIO-VASCULAR SYSTEM

Close your hand into a fist and look at it. Your fist is approximately the same size as your heart, around 12 cm long, 9 cm wide and 6 cm thick. It is located behind the sternum and tilted to the left. The heart is made up mainly of cardiac muscle, which is also known as **myocardium**.

Anatomy of the heart

The heart is divided into right- and the left-hand sides by the **septum** (see Figure 7.35). It is further divided into four chambers. The upper two chambers are called **atria**. The atria receive blood returning to the heart via the veins. The lower two chambers are called **ventricles**, and these act as pumps to squeeze blood out of the heart into the arteries.

FIGURE 7.35 The heart

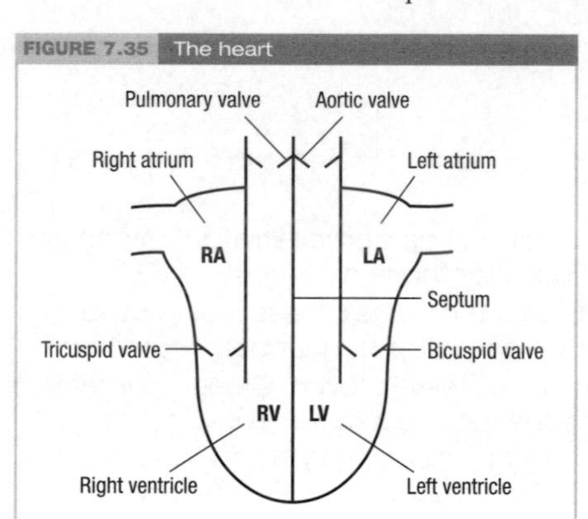

- **Right atrium (RA)** – This receives deoxygenated blood from the organs of the body.
- **Right ventricle (RV)** – This pumps deoxygenated blood to
the lungs.
- **Left atrium (LA)** – This receives oxygenated blood from the lungs.
- **Left ventricle (LV)** – This pumps oxygenated blood to all organs of the body. It is larger and therefore stronger than the right ventricle as it has to pump the blood through the body.
- **Valves** – There are four one-way valves in the heart, that open or close in response to pressure of blood flow:

  - bicuspid valve – separates the left atrium from the left ventricle
  - tricuspid valve – separates the right atrium from the right ventricle
  - aortic valve – separates the left ventricle from the aorta
  - pulmonary valve – separates the right ventricle from the pulmonary artery.

All these valves ensure that blood flows in one direction and prevent the back flow of blood into the ventricles.

The blood vessels leading to and from the heart are as follows.

- The **aorta** carries oxygenated blood out of the left ventricle to the body.
- The superior **vena cava** returns deoxygenated blood to the right atrium from the head and upper body; the inferior vena cava returns deoxygenated blood to the right atrium from the lower body.
- The **pulmonary vein** carries freshly oxygenated blood from the lungs to the left atrium.
- The **pulmonary artery** carries deoxygenated blood from the body to the lungs.

FIGURE 7.36 Blood flow through the heart

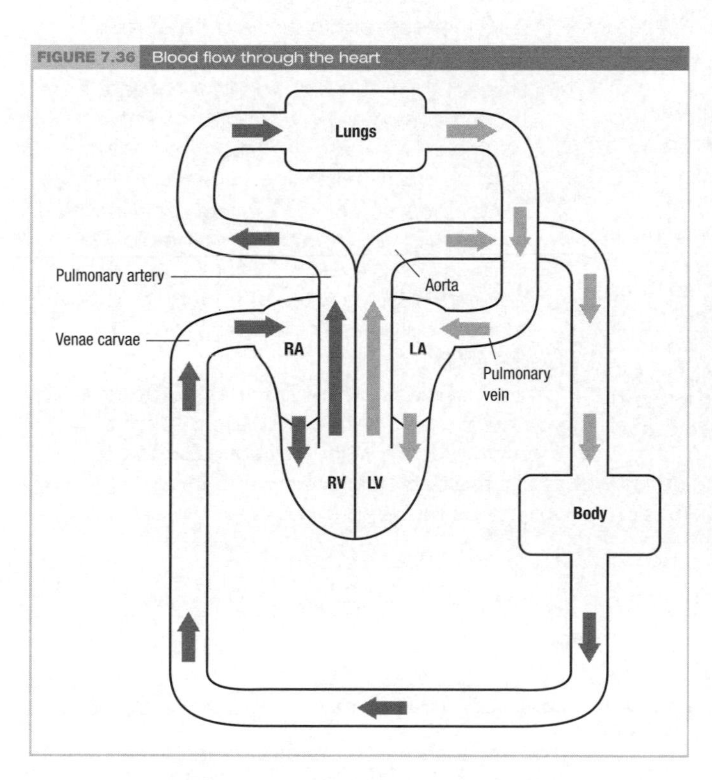

Blood flow through the heart

Pulmonary circulation

The right ventricle pumps blood through the pulmonary artery to the lungs (see Figure 7.36). Here, the blood 'picks up' oxygen and carbon dioxide is released into the lungs. From the lungs, the oxygenated blood is carried to the left atrium. This short loop is called the **pulmonary circulation**.

Systemic circulation

From the left atrium the blood flows down to the left ventricle. The left ventricle pumps oxygenated blood through the Aorta to all tissues of the body (see Figure 7.36). Oxygen and nutrients are released from the blood to nourish cells, and carbon dioxide and other waste products are carried back to the heart via the two venae cavae. The blood enters the right atrium. Carbon dioxide is carried to the lungs and removed from the body.

STUDENT PRACTICAL

Heart dissection

Aim

The aim of this practical is to examine the structure of a mammalian heart.

Equipment

sheep or pig hearts
tweezers
scissors
latex gloves
disposal bag/bin for hearts and used gloves
dissection boards
scalpels
lab coats
disinfectant
worksheets

Method

Working in groups of three or four put on lab coats, goggles and latex gloves then complete the following activities.

1 Examine the outside of the heart and make a note of its texture and appearance.
2 Try to determine the orientation of the heart in the body.
3 The valves inside the heart should still be intact and can be shown to still work. Go to a sink and pass running water into the left and right atria; it should be possible to see the valves close.
4 Place the heart back on the dissection board, dome side up, and make an incision with the scalpel or with the scissors from the right atrium right down to the right ventricle. This should expose the whole of the inside of the right-hand side of the heart. Make a note of the appearance and texture of the inside of the heart.
5 The tendons that hold the valves in place can be seen clearly. Use the tweezers to pull on these, and make a note of their strength.
6 Dissect the left-hand side of the heart, from the left atrium down towards the left ventricle. Compare the thickness of the right- and left-hand side ventricle walls.
7 Try to ascertain which blood vessel is which by pushing your finger down the blood vessels into the heart. Where your finger appears should give you enough of a clue to work out which blood vessel is which.

Conclusion

In your conclusion look, back at the comments you have made throughout the dissection, then write down what you have found out about the heart's anatomy and try to explain why it has these anatomical features.

STUDENT ACTIVITY

Structure of the heart

Fill in the blanks

The heart is split into _______ sides and has ______ chambers. The top two chambers are called ____ and the bottom two chambers are called __________. The heart is split into two separate sides by the __________.

There are _____ valves that allow the blood to pass through the heart in one direction.

The valve between the atrium and ventricle on the right side of the heart is called the __________ valve. The valve on the left side of the heart between the atrium and the ventricle, is called the ________ valve. The valve between the pulmonary artery and right ventricle is called the _________ valve. The valve between the left ventricle and the aorta is called the ________ valve.

Types of blood vessels

Blood travels through a series of vessels, each varies in structure because of its function. There are five categories of blood vessel:

- artery
- arteriole
- capillary
- venuole
- vein.

The blood travels through these vessels in the above order.

Structure of arteries and arterioles

An artery carries blood under high pressure away from the heart. An arteriole has basically the same structure as an artery, except an artery is bigger. They both have a strong outer layer, a thick middle layer made of smooth muscle and a thin lininig or inner layer made of endothelium (see Figure 7.37).

FIGURE 7.37 Structure of arteries and arterioles

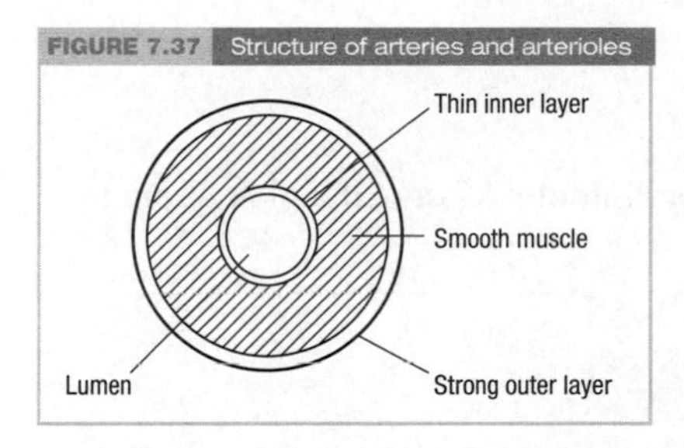

As the arteries get smaller and become arterioles, the greater the amount of smooth muscle they contain. This increase in smooth muscle allows the blood vessels to dilate (vasodilation) or constrict (vasoconsriction) depending on whether areas of the body require more or less blood.

Capillaries

FIGURE 7.38 Structure of a capillary

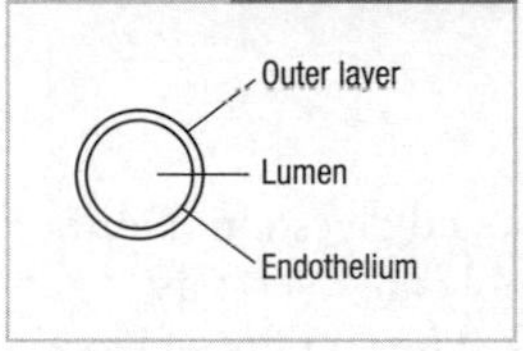

Outer layer
Lumen
Endothelium

Capillaries are the smallest blood vessels in the body. It is in the capillaries that the gases and nutrients leave and/or enter the bloodstream. As this is where the 'action' occurs, the capillaries will only allow blood through them one red blood cell at a time. Capillaires are not only very narrow, but they also have very thin walls which allow for easier diffusion of gases and nutrients through them (see Figure 7.38).

Veins and venuoles

Veins and venuoles return blood under low pressure back to the heart. They have a very similar structure to arteries and arterioles except that they have a much thinner layer of smooth muscle in their walls. Veins also contain one-way valves to help ensure blood flows in one direction back to the heart.

Blood

An average adult male has 5 litres of blood in his body, which accounts for approximately 8% of his total body weight. Blood is made up of four main things:

- plasma
- red blood cells (erythrocytes)
- white blood cells (leucocytes)
- platelets.

Plasma makes up 55% of the blood volume. It is yellow in colour and conisists mainly of water. However, dissolved in plasma you will also find the following substances:

- oxygen and carbon dioxide
- salts
- glucose
- fatty acids
- waste products.

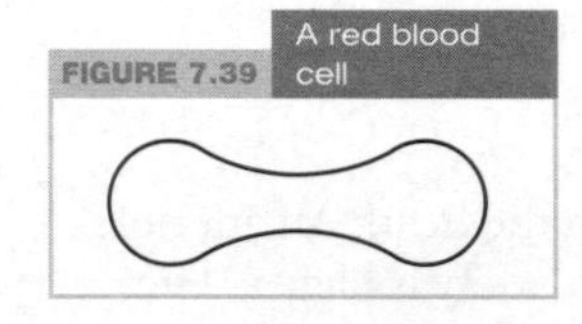

FIGURE 7.39 A red blood cell

Red blood cells are responsible for making blood its red colour. Their main function is to transport oxygen around the body. They contain a protein called **haemoglobin** which picks up oxygen and carries it to where it is needed. A red blood cell is a biconcave disc shape and contains no nucleus (see Figure 7.39).

White blood cells are responsible for protecting the body from infection.

Platelets aid in clotting blood, which is necessary if we cut ourselves.

Distribution of blood

At rest, cardiac output is about 5 litres per minute. Most of the blood from the heart goes to six major organs:

- brain 0.75 l
- heart 0.25 l
- kidneys 1.25 l
- skeletal muscle 1.00 l
- gastrointestinal (GI) tract 1.25 l
- skin 0.50 l

After a meal, more blood goes to the GI tract in order to aid digestion. During physical activity, more blood goes to the muscles to supply the necessary nutrients and oxygen and take away the waste produces. The amount of blood to the brain, however, is constant at all times.

The lungs

Structure of the lungs

Pulmonary ventilation is the term used to describe the process of bringing the surrounding air into the body and exchanging it with the air in the lungs. The average lung has a volume of 4–6 l and weighs approximately 1 kg. Lungs have a very large surface area, which means that if you were to dissect a person's lungs and spread them out on the ground they would cover 60–80 m^2, which is the equivalent of half a tennis court!

The lungs are enclosed by a set of membranes known as the **pleura**, which are arranged like a double-skinned bag. The visceral pleura are found on the outer

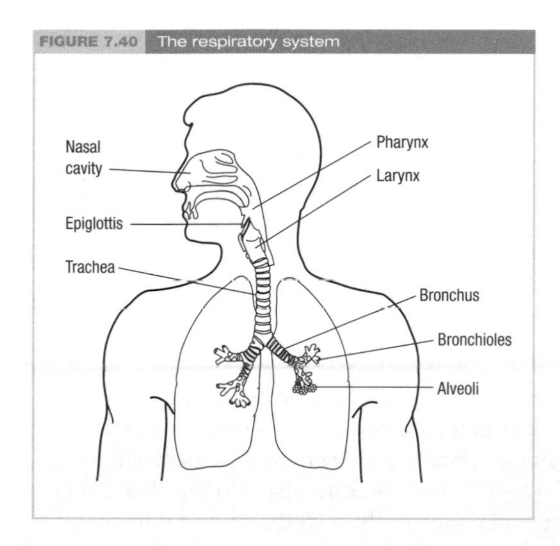

FIGURE 7.40 The respiratory system

surface of lungs and the parietal pleura line the chest cavity. In between these two pleura there is a lubricating fluid called **pleural fluid**, which helps the two pleura to glide over each other as the lungs continually expand and contract.

The lungs consist of lots of different tubes through which the air flows (see Figure 7.40). Air enters the body through the **nose and mouth**. The air is warmed and filtered in the nose, and then passes into the **pharynx** (throat) and then into the **larynx** (voice box). The **epiglottis** is a flap of cartilage which prevents food from entering the trachea (windpipe). The air then passes into the **trachea**, which is a tubular passageway approximately 12 cm long and 2.5 cm wide. It has horse-shoe shaped rings of cartilage (hyaline cartilage) that keep the airway open. In between the rings of cartilage lies smooth muscle. From the trachea the air passes into the right and left **bronchi**, which are large tubes passing into the lungs. Each bronchus further divides into smaller tubes called **bronchioles**, which are made of smooth muscle. Eventually these tubes connect to the **alveoli**, which are like micro-sized bundles of grapes at the end of the respiratory tract.

The alveoli provide a huge surface area for **gaseous exchange** (swapping of oxygen and carbon dioxide) to take place. They are surrounded by a dense network of capillaries and gases are able to **diffuse** easily through the very thin semi-permeable walls of the alveoli and the blood vessels. Oxygen diffuses from the alveoli into the blood, and carbon dioxide diffuses from the blood to the alveoli. **Gaseous exchange** takes less than a second to occur. Breathing alters the composition of air by changing the proportions of the gases it contains (see Table 7.3).

Table 7.3 Effect of gaseous exchange on air

Gas	Air breathed in	Air breathed out
Oxygen	21%	16%
Carbon dioxide	0.04%	4%
Nitrogen	78%	78%

Mechanics of breathing

The muscles involved in breathing are the **diaphragm** and the external and internal **intercostals**. The intercostal muscles are between the ribs. The internal intercostal muscles contract to pull the ribs downwards and so help with breathing out. The external intercostal muslces pull the ribs upwards and therefore assist with breathing in. The diaphragm is a large, dome-shaped muscle located beneath the lungs; it is responsible for approximately 75% of the breathing mechanism.

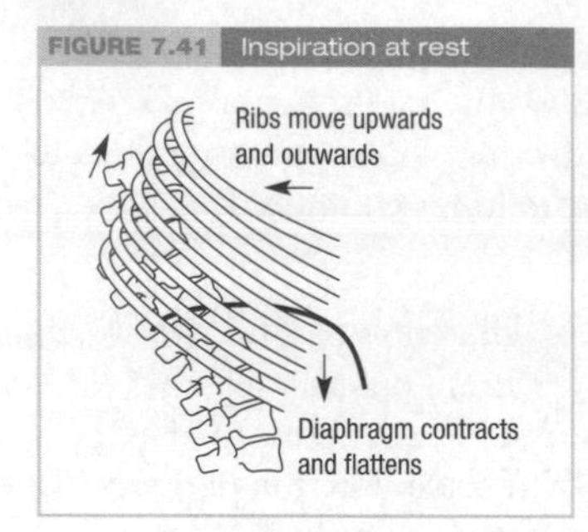

Inspiration at rest

During **inspiration** (breathing in) the diaphragm contracts and moves downwards, and the external intercostal muscles contract, moving the ribs and sternum upwards and outwards (see Figure 7.41). As a consequence of this the chest cavity enlarges. This increase in space reduces the pressure in the lungs in relation to atmospheric pressure. This change in pressure inside the lungs results in the air being drawn into the lungs from the atmosphere, inflating the lungs until the pressure in the lungs is equal to the atmospheric pressure.

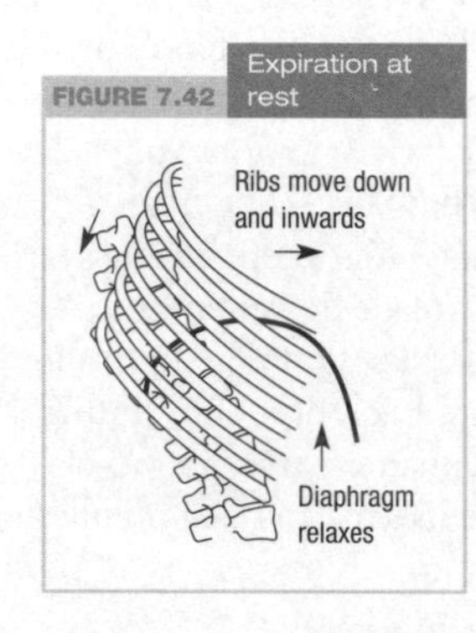

Expiration at rest

Expiration (breathing out) does not require any muscle contraction and is called a passive activity. The lungs that have been stretched recoil and the diaphragm relaxes. The sternum and ribs move downwards as the diaphragm moves upwards (see Figure 7.42). This decreases the space in the chest cavity and squeezes the air out of the lungs and out through the nose and mouth.

Lung volumes and capacities

A number of different names are given to the various amounts of air we breath in and out in different circumstances. Some of these volumes can be measured using a spirometer.

1. **Tidal volume (TV 500 ml)** – This is the volume of air moved with each breath. Breathe in and out normally; the amount of air you have breathed in and out is your tidal volume. This volume will change depending on whether you are at rest or exercising. Exercise usually results in an increase in the tidal volume.
2. **Residual volume (RV 1200 ml)** – Breath out as hard as possible. The amount of air that remains in the lungs after full expiration is your residual volume and is necessary in order to prevent your lungs collapsing.
3. **Vital capacity (VC 5000 ml)** – The VC is the amount of air that can be expired after maximum inspiration.
4. **Forced expiratory volume (FEV)** – This is the volume of air forcibly exhaled in the first second after maximal inhalation. It should be around 80% of vital capacity, values less than this indicate asthma or bronchial problems.
5. **Inspiratory Reserve Volume (IRV 3,000 ml)** – This is the maximal volume of air inspired after the end of inspiration.
6. **Expiratory Reserve Volume (ERV normal 1200 ml)** – This is the maximal volume of air breathed out at the end of the normal inspiration.
7. **Total Lung capacity (TLC 6000 ml)** – This is the sum of all lung volumes.

8 **Minute ventilation (VE 7500 ml)** – This is the volume of air breathed in and out per minute.

These values will all depend on a variety of factors, including:

- size of lungs/ribcage, which is genetically determined
- strength of respiratory muscles
- resistance to airflow in bronchioles and alveoli as a result of lung disorders, colds and smoking.

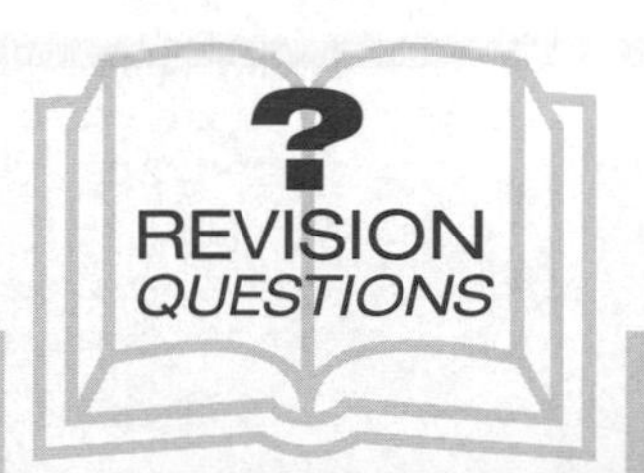

1) What is the function of the heart?
2) Why is the heart some times called a 'double pump'?
3) Which heart chamber contains the thickest myocardium? Why do you think this is?
4) Why are valves necessary inside the heart?
5) List the blood vessels leading to and from the heart through which the blood flows.
6) Give a brief account of how the structure of arteries, arterioles, capillaries, venuoles and veins is related to their function.
7) What is blood made up of?
8) Describe which structures air flows through on its way from the mouth to the alveoli.
9) Explain the mechanics of breathing in and out.
10) What happens to tidal volume during exercise? Explain why this occurs.

1) Explain how the muscles work with the skeleton in order to produce movement.
2) Give examples of how a sports person produces different types of muscle contraction during a game of rugby.
3) How do the respiratory system and cardiovascular system supply oxygen to the working muscles?
4) What are the different types of muscle tissue and where could you find them?
5) What happens to blood flow to the various organs during exericse and how is it controlled?

FURTHER READING

Blakey, P. (2000) *The Muscle Book*. Himalayan Institute Press
Kingston, B. (2000) *Understanding Joints*. Stanley Thornes.
Kingston, B. (1998) *Understanding Muscles*. Stanley Thornes
Seeley, R. R., Stephens, T. D., Tate, P. (2000) *Anatomy and Physiology*. McGraw Hill
Stone, R. J., Stone, J. A., (1999) *Atlas of Skeletal Muscles*. McGraw Hill

QUANTITATIVE AND QUALITATIVE SPORT AND EXERCISE RESEARCH

CHAPTER 9

This chapter explains methods used in **quantitative** and **qualitative** research by sport and exercise scientists. It will enable you to understand research in all disciplines of sport and exercise science. It should allow you to develop research skills, including collecting data, handling data, mathematical and statistical skills that will be required by you to carry out your own research. Numbers and mathematical concepts put off a lot of students, but the purpose of research methods and statistics is to help you understand and interpret the meaning of sets of numbers. The major difference between quantitative research and qualitative research is that quantitative research is based more on numerical evidence (numbers, e.g. heart rate) while qualitative research places more emphasis on what people do or say (e.g. answers given in an interview).

By the end of this chapter you should be able to:

- review types of quantitative data
- review types of qualitative data and issues relating to them
- collect sport and exercise science quantitative research data
- plan to collect sport and exercise science qualitative research data
- interpret quantitative research results
- collect and interpret qualitative research results
- present sport and exercise science quantitative research using IT
- present the sport and exercise science qualitative research using IT.

TYPES AND QUALITY OF DATA

Classification

A group or set of numbers is referred to as data. The resting heart rates of a group of people would be a set of data. Data can include more than one type of measurement, for example, the height and weight of a number people. Each different type of measurement is called a **variable**, because the value of the measurement can vary. In sport and exercise a variable is something that we measure (e.g. blood pressure, anxiety levels, flexibility). If the variable can be recorded using a number it is described as a **numeric variable**. However, not all variables or sets of data have to use numbers. An example of this would be recording the gender of a group of people – instead of numbers, labels would be used (male and female). Variables with letters or words in place of numbers are called **string variables.**

Numbers can be classified according to their level of measurement. The most basic type of numeric measurement uses a nominal scale, where nominal value (a number) is assigned to a category. If gender is to be recorded in a table, males could be denoted by a 2 and females by a 1. These values would be nominal; that is, classification is for identification purposes only. Values are assigned arbitrarily and are nominated by the measurer. The values have no numerical meaning, so 2 is not twice as good as 1. They are just labels to distinguish each category. **Nominal data** is sometimes referred to as **discrete data**, because you can only have discrete values (e.g. male or female, yes or no).

A second type of numeric measurement is ordinal. **Ordinal values** occur when numbers are assigned to categories, and these numbers indicate rank (e.g. Liverpool = 1st, Leeds = 2nd, Man Utd = 3rd). In the example given each number indicates football league position, that is Liverpool is first, Leeds is second and so on. This sort of data provides us with more information than nominal data (e.g. we can now say who is the tallest, quickest or heaviest). It is important to note that the distance between categories is still unknown. In the league position example, the team in first place maybe one point ahead of the team in second, while the team in second could be three points in front of the team in third. This type of data only gives a rank order (i.e. first, second, third) and not an exact value.

A further type of numerical variable is that given by **interval** or **ratio level** data. These are actually two different classifications of data, but due to their many similarities can be referred to as one. An interval scale has equal distances between values and is an accepted unit of physical measurement, for example, the Fahrenheit scale. It is different from a ratio scale in that it has an arbitrary zero point. Ratio scales have a zero point determined by nature (e.g. time, distance, weight) or what is called an absolute zero. Therefore, a distance of 20 km is twice that of 10 km. The same cannot be said for Fahrenheit, that is, 20°F is not twice has hot as 10°F. Interval or ratio data is continuous. Continuous data can have any numeric value with any number of decimal places. The time taken to run the 100 m would be a continuous measure (e.g. a value of 11.43 secs). Interval or ratio data can be converted into ordinal or nominal scales. If you were to measure the precise height of subjects, you could then categorise the subjects into the following groups based on their height: tall = 1, medium height = 2, short = 3. This would be converting ratio data into ordinal data.

Data classification

Determine the levels of measurement of the following variables and give explanations for why you have chosen each particular classification.

1 blood pressure
2 compliance with an exercise programme:
   a) followed programme = 1
   b) dropped out = 2
3 finishing time:
   a) < 10 secs = 1
   b) 10–20 secs = 2
   c) >20 secs = 3
4 heart rate
5 distance walked

Primary and secondary data

Why do we need to take measurements in sport and exercise science? Measurement allows us to quantify things (e.g. it is possible to give a value for the number of times a heart beats in a minute). With sufficient measurement, data can be produced, so heart rate over a given time could be displayed. The production of data is important in science as it allows analysis; hence, it would be possible to examine what happens to heart rate during a set time period or in a given situation (e.g. during exercise). Does heart rate increase, decrease, or stay the same during exercise? This analysis in turn allows interpretation to infer meaning. The reason for an increased heart rate could be examined. Why did the heart rate go up? What caused it?

Data that you measure yourself is called **primary data**; somebody else's data that you use is would be secondary data. If you were examining the number of yellow and red cards for the teams competing in the last three football world cups, you would need to collect the data from these world cups. This might involve looking up information on the internet, for example. This would be secondary data, which is originally recorded by somebody other than you.

Quality of data

Accuracy and precision

If you are a sport and exercise scientist testing and assessing athletes, you need to take special care when interpreting results of tests. Because people can only measure something to a certain degree of accuracy, it is important to realise that a measurement always has some level of uncertainty. This depends on the precision of the measuring device. For example, if you weigh two people on a bathroom scale, the bathroom scale may show that both weigh 75 kg. But if you weigh the two on a digital set of scales, the digital scales may show that one weighs 74.88 kg while the other weighs 75.21 kg. Could it be said that these two people have the same mass?

Precision is related to the care and refinement of the measuring process. It is assessed via the repeatability of the readings. Precision can be observed by duplicating a measurement (i.e. taking a number of readings of the same thing, e.g. measuring a person's height three times). When the number of repetitions of a measurement, using a specific method, is sufficiently high, a statistical measure of precision can be computed (called standard deviation).

Accuracy determines conformity with the truth or with a gold standard. Are you recording the actual value of something as you intended? If you were measuring heart rate with a heart rate monitor and it was displaying a value of 144 beats per minute (bpm), yet the real heart rate was 150 bpm the monitor would be inaccurate. **Validity** is a measure of accuracy (see below). Accuracy relates to the quality of a result, and is distinguished from precision, which relates to the quality of the operation by which the result is obtained. A measurement can be precise but inaccurate, as well as accurate but imprecise. For example, if a measurement was made with care, using a highly refined piece of equipment, repeated readings of the same quantity would agree closely and thus precision would exist (recording the mass of a person three times with readings of 80.6, 80.3 and 80.4kg is an example). However, if the instrument was calibrated incorrectly the results would be inaccurate (so, let us say the scales are consistently giving results that are 2 kg too high, the true readings would have been 78.6, 78.3 and 78.4kg).

FIGURE 9.1 Targets showing various degrees of accuracy and precision

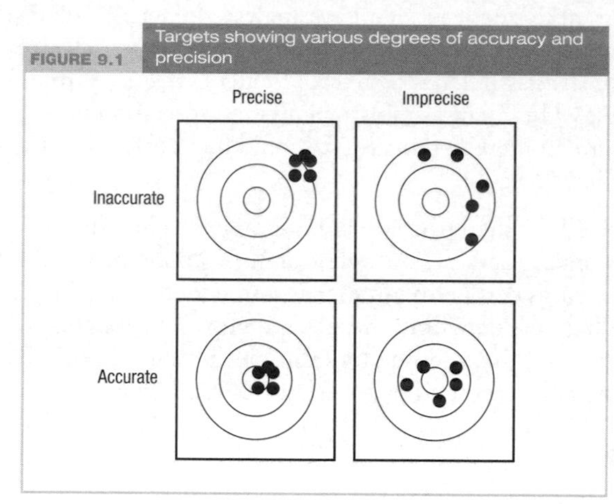

An easy way to illustrate the difference between accuracy and precision is to use the analogy of a marksman. For the marksman the truth (or the gold standard) is represented by the bull's-eye. Precision relates to the quality of an operation by which a result is obtained, and is distinguished from accuracy, which relates to the quality of the result. In Figure 9.1, the top left target, the marksman has achieved uniformity (good precision), although it is inaccurate. In the bottom right target, the marksman has grouped shots around the bull's-eye, but without great precision. The bottom left target represents both accuracy and precision. It differs from the top left target in that the degree of precision has not changed greatly, but its closeness to the bull's-eye (the truth) has improved.

Error

As can be seen by examining accuracy and precision, measurement is inexact. The amount of this in exactness is called the error. In research, an error is not a mistake; a mistake would be due to carelessness. Error is a part of measurement, and incorporates such things as the precision of the measuring equipment, its calibration and competent use. Errors are unavoidable even for the most carefully trained and determined researcher.

There are two types of errors: systematic and random. **Systematic errors** are predictable, correctable and, as such, avoidable. **Random errors**, however, are unavoidable because of imperfections in measurement systems. Random errors can be controlled and minimised, but not eliminated. Systematic errors are constant and can usually be attributed to instrument maladjustment, lack of calibration, or the environment. If they are discovered, they can be quantified and via calibration they can be corrected. Random errors are so named because they follow random patterns (the laws of chance). Although the magnitude of a random error is unknown, it can be estimated. These errors are caused by human and equipment flaws, as well as the effects of the environment on measurements. Random errors occur naturally, even when the individual is attempting to perform the procedure correctly.

Errors can result from a number of sources.

- **Natural errors** result from measurements that are made in uncontrollable environments. They are affected by such factors as temperature, humidity, atmospheric pressure, heat, wind and gravity. If you were measuring heart rate in a warm room, it would be elevated due to the requirements of thermoregulation; this would have to be taken into consideration when discussing any results.
- A second source of error is **instrumental errors**. Most measurements make use of variety of apparatus; error is always present in the measurements due to imperfections in the equipment.
- **Personal errors** are another area for consideration. Humans are nearly always directly involved with measurements and therefore human errors are inevitable.
- Finally **calculation errors** exist. Round-off errors can occur when sufficient digits are not recorded and carried through all calculations. Significant figures recorded while measuring directly affect the significant figures in calculated results.

Care needs to be taken when recording error, since error scores can be misleading. Imagine you were conducting an experiment that required subjects to move forward to a target, your error scores would have both plus and minus values. A situation could arise whereby a subject is 10 cm short of the target on the first attempt (the error would be recorded as –10 cm) and then 10 cm over on the second attempt (recorded as 10 cm). Overall, if the mean error is calculated the two error values have cancelled each other out, the mean error being 0 cm. This type of error recording is termed **relative error**. A more realistic measure would be **absolute error**. This is the average absolute deviation away from the target, irrespective of direction. Therefore, in the above example (being 10 cm short and then 10 cm over), the absolute error would be 10 cm in both cases giving a mean absolute error of 10 cm, quite a difference from the relative error of 0 cm.

Reliability

This is a measure of how repeatable a set of data is. That is, if you measured the same thing on separate occasions, would you record the same value. Imagine you were coaching a cyclist, and to monitor his training and recovery you recorded his resting heart rate each morning. Assuming your cyclist was not overtraining or suffering from an illness, you would expect the resting heart rate to remain fairly constant over a number of weeks. If you measured similar values each morning this would display good reliability. You would then be assured that your measuring technique was reliable. If the values did change, you could then be sure it was due to something other than your measuring – your athlete may be suffering from a cold, which might have elevated their resting heart rate.

The two biggest causes of unreliability in sport and exercise research are errors and **intra-subject variation**. Error, as previously mentioned, can be caused by poor or inaccurate equipment or the inability of the tester to use the equipment correctly. These can easily be overcome with adequate maintenance and the right training. The second factor affecting reliability, intra-subject variation, is harder to control. Even when measuring physiological variables using accurate equipment it is difficult to record exactly the same value due to variations within each subject. From day to day people eat different amounts, sleep for different lengths of time, undertake different levels of physical activity, have differing mental states and so on. So, resting heart rate will vary from day to day due to these factors. Researchers try and minimise these effects by standardising the testing situation. In the above example you could record heart rate at the same time each morning, before breakfast and before the person has had the opportunity to be affected by what happens that day, both physiologically and psychologically. It is also common for researchers to make repeated observations and report the average value, thus averaging out any errors or variations.

Validity

Validity refers to the meaningfulness of a set of data. Did you measure what you set out to measure? You may have decided, as a cricket coach, to measure the aerobic fitness of your players by getting them to perform the bleep test. Your results may be very reliable, but are they valid (that is, do the results of the bleep test relate to levels of fitness in your players)? This is a difficult question to answer. It is often difficult, especially in a **field setting**, to measure exactly the variable you are looking at. A cricket coach could not practically measure the aerobic capacity (VO_2max) of his players, but he could quite easily measure their performance on the bleep test and relate it back to VO_2max values (see page 314).

Choosing a valid test can be a problem in sport and exercise science research. All too often people use a test to measure certain variables, then make generalisations based on the results, which can lack validity. For example, the sit and reach test is often used to measure flexibility, however, it only incorporates leg and back flexibility. Even then there is debate about its usefulness in measuring this. So, to make statements about an athlete's overall flexibility based on one test (the sit and reach test) would be incorrect; it would

not be valid. When making claims regarding measurements it is therefore very important to be specific about such claims or to have a wide range of measurements on which to base any statements.

Objectivity

If a similar measurement is obtained by two different experimenters it is said to be objective. As a measure of the number of times your heart beats, heart rate recorded at the radial artery is an objective measure. Two different people would obtain similar values when measuring somebody's pulse. It is a simple matter of counting the number of beats in a given time, then converting this to beats per minute. Measuring blood pressure (at the brachial artery with a manual sphygmomanometer) would be less objective. For example, the person measuring blood pressure has to decide the value of systolic pressure based on when they can hear a constant tapping sound (the Kortikoff sounds). Similarly, diastolic pressure is recorded on the absence of a rhythmic tapping sound. Both these points will be slightly subjective, that is, different people could record them differently.

In sport and exercise, measuring systems are designed to be objective; however, there are times when this is not always possible. Physiological measures tend to display the greatest objectivity. The most difficult areas in which to gain objectivity are when an opinion is required or when people are expected to judge performance. For example, scoring in gymnastics can be subjective. Detailed scoring systems, involving a number of judges, have been developed to try and overcome this problem.

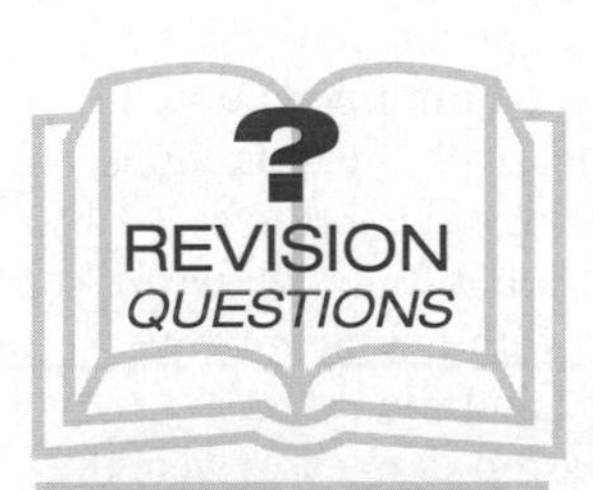

1) Give two examples of the different types of data.
2) How do accuracy and precision differ? Give a sporting example to illustrate your answer.
3) Explain the difference between absolute and relative error.

Accuracy/precision and validity/reliability

The following is a set of body fat percentage values recorded on a group of people using body fat callipers. Body fat was measured at two different times during the day. Body fat was also recorded via under-water weighing (considered to give a truer value of % body fat).

Subject	1	2	3	4	5	6	7	8
Body fat % (callipers a.m.)	22	15	13	11	26	26	27	13
Body fat % (callipers p.m.)	21	15	14	10	24	25	27	12
Body fat % (under water)	25	17	14	12	28	29	31	16

1 How could you determine the precision of the body fat callipers?
2 How precise are they?
3 How could you establish how accurate they are?
4 How accurate are they?
5 Review the results of the body fat callipers in terms of reliability and validity.
6 How could reliability and validity be assessed?
7 How do reliability and validity relate to accuracy and precision?

Ethical and legal issues

A lot of testing, measuring and research in sport and exercise science involves working with other people (athletes, clients of a health club, etc.). It is important to respect the rights of other people and ensure they are not negatively affected by your tests or work. This is especially true when working with children. Your subjects should be made aware of their right to withdraw from a test or programme of exercise. The decision to take part in an activity is down to the individual (if they decide to stop the test, then you must comply with their wishes). It is therefore necessary to explain the full procedures and plans of an activity, and inform them of others who maybe involved in the activity. This will enable subjects to be aware of what is happening, and will ensure that an individual's performance on a test is limited only by what is being measured, and not by a lack of understanding in how to perform the test. It is also essential to make clear that any information taken or recorded about a subject will be confidential.

It may be necessary to prove that the above considerations have been adhered to. For example, you may be conducting some research at a local health club, and one of the clients is injured while undergoing a fitness test. The manager of the club will want to know if it was your testing that caused the injury. In such a case it is not only important that you have stuck to certain guidelines while testing, but that you can show this to be the case. This is the reason that informed consent forms are used in research and testing situations. An **informed consent** form is a signed agreement demonstrating that the subject has both been informed of the test (told of what is going to happen) and has given their consent (agreed to undertake the test). A good informed consent form should outline the risks and discomforts associated with the tests, along with any expected benefits from taking part in the testing. The form should also highlight that permission to take part in the test is voluntary and that, having given initial consent to take part, the subject is free to withdraw at any time. The procedures of the test should be clearly explained and should be understandable to the subject. For example, with children or in cases were the test is very detailed or complicated, the procedures should be simplified. The subjects should be told to ask about anything they do not understand, or if they have any concerns regarding the testing. Finally, it is crucial that the subject signs the form to say they have read and understood it and are willing to take part in the testing.

Data protection

As mentioned previously, any information on a subject, athlete or client should be kept confidential. This is in line with the Data Protection Act, which was last updated in 1998. Records (hard copy or computerised) should be kept where only authorised personnel can access them. When reporting information to third parties, personal details should be omitted. For example, if you were reporting back to a group of athletic coaches regarding some research you had done on strength training, you would not include in your report or presentation

the names of the subjects you had used. It would be sufficient for you to give general background information, such as age, gender, ability level, years of training and so on.

Treatment, variables

When collecting information or data you will have a research problem or question you are trying to answer. A research problem is a statement that asks what relation exists between two or more variables. For instance, what effect does exercise have on heart rate? Remember, a variable is something measurable, in this case the amount of exercise and the subject's heart rate. The thing that you are trying to affect, and that you are uncertain of, is called the **dependent variable** (in this example, heart rate). It is dependant upon the other variable, that is, your heart rate depends on the amount of exercise you do. The variable you have control over is the **independent variable** (exercise, in this case). The independent variable is termed the **treatment**; you control it to determine what effect it has on the dependant variable.

Research design

There are a number of steps involved in designing a research project.

1. First, you need to develop the problem or arrive at the question(s) you want answers to (e.g. How does exercise affect heart rate?).
2. Step two is to formulate the **hypothesis**. What you think will happen, based on previous evidence that you have researched (e.g. heart rate increases with exercise).
3. The next step would be to gather information or collect the data (e.g. measure heart rate during exercise).
4. Finally you will need to analyse and interpret the results to see if your expectations are correct (e.g. Does heart rate go up and by how much?).

Good research problems should:

- be a question
- be open to testing
- be of interest
- be of practical value.

The most common type of research design is to have two groups, one undergoing a treatment and the other being the **control group** (having no treatment). Both groups are measured on a variable(s) pre- and post-treatment. This is termed a pre-test post-test research design. For example, if you wanted to determine if relaxation reduced anxiety before an examination, you could have two groups. Group one would receive relaxation treatment, while group two would have no treatment. It would then be possible to create the hypothesis for this investigation. Rather than just saying relaxation affects anxiety it is usual in research methods to state three hypotheses: the null hypothesis, the alternative

hypothesis and the directional hypotheses. In the above example the hypothesis would be expressed as follows:

- **Null hypothesis**: there will be no difference in pre-examination anxiety between groups one and two.
- **Alternative hypothesis**: there will be a difference in pre-examination anxiety between the two groups.
- **Directional hypothesis**: group one (who undergo relaxation) will rate their pre-examination anxiety lower than will group two (the control group).

Not all research uses the pre-test post-test design. Sometimes there may not be a treatment, or not one you impose. You might wish to examine how much sport and physical education children do in schools and the effect it has on the sport they take part in outside of school. In this case the dependent variable (the thing you are measuring) is how much sport is played outside of school. The independent variable (normally the treatment or the thing you change) would be the amount of sport and physical education done in school. Obviously you cannot change this; it is determined by the school, local education authority and the government. What you can do is compare one school with another, one area with another, or even compare countries (e.g. France v England). This is termed a **comparative study** and is more common in the sociological area of sport and exercise.

A similar method is to compare evidence, data or information over time, instead of comparing one region with another. You may wish to see how the amount of physical education in schools has changed over the years. This method works if you have the data or can obtain it, but in some instances for what you hope to measure there may be little or no data. If this is the case, you would have to set up a study to examine things in the future. Let us imagine you wish to see the effect of school sport and physical education on the health of children in your area. However, you have no information on the current state of health of the children. What you would have to do is monitor the sport and physical education participated in by the children, and their level of health. You would have to do this over a period of time to see if their health improved, declined or stayed the same. This type of study is called a **longitudinal study**. It is often used in the study of health and disease. Unfortunately, it requires time for any effects of changes to be seen – some longitudinal research can last for over 30 years. Therefore, this method would not be suitable for a small research project (the sort of project outlined in Chapter 2).

Questionnaire design

A widespread method of obtaining data in both qualitative and quantitative research is the questionnaire. A questionnaire is a survey used in research in which information is obtained by asking subjects to respond to questions. The major limitation with a questionnaire is that the results consist of what people say they do or believe, and this is not always reliable. Therefore, careful planning is needed to ensure valid results. Sometimes researchers use

techniques to try and identify whether people are telling the truth. This is difficult, but one way it can be done in a questionnaire is by repeating questions or asking very similar questions. If a person is telling the truth or answering each question properly (and not just skimming through the questions) you would expect the same answer to these repeated or similar questions.

It is important to consider what you wish to obtain from the questionnaire (i.e. what information you hope to collect). Careful consideration also needs to be given to the actual questions asked. For example, there are two general types of questions that could be asked in a questionnaire, closed questions and open questions. A **closed question** is one where you only give a certain number of options and the respondent has to pick from them. An example would be 'How do you rate your fitness?', with the possible answers being; not at all fit, slightly fit, moderately fit, very fit or extremely fit. You know the answer will be from this list. With an open question there is no such list; the question is open-ended (e.g. How could you improve your level of fitness?). In this case the range of possible answers is almost endless. A further concern is the order in which you put the questions. Often questionnaires collect general information first, things like age, gender, job, sport played and so on. This gets people in to the habit of answering the questions. They are more likely then to complete the questionnaire. If the questions become more difficult or detailed it may be necessary to give examples. A major problem with research involving questionnaires is people either not completing the questionnaire sufficiently or not completing it at all.

To obtain the best results from a questionnaire it should be relatively short, as you are more likely to get a response. You also need to think about how you are going to present your results. A lot of open questions may give you lots of information in return, but this will be hard to summarise in a table or graph. Too many open questions are difficult to analyse and are time consuming. Numerical data is easier to analyse, so you should try and code or score the possible answers (e.g. yes = 2, no = 1). There are different ways that questions can be coded. **Scaled questions** use what is called a Likert scale, which is a level of agreement or rating with a given statement. Using the previous example on fitness, the following is a scaled question: How do you rate your fitness?

Not at all fit	Slightly fit	Moderately fit	Very fit	Extremely fit
1	2	3	4	5

With a scaled question you are looking for one answer that best fits the level the respondent feels they are at. It maybe that you are seeking more than one answer, in which case you could use a ranking questions. **Ranking questions** place alternatives in order. An example could be, 'Which sport do you enjoy participating in most?', where 1 is the most preferred and 5 is the least, and where the options are basketball, rugby, cricket, running and cycling. The respondent would then rate each sport from 1 to 5 based on their level of enjoyment of that sport. **Categorical questions** are used when a discreet answer is required, so a choice of categories is offered. For example:

Have you ever been skiing?	Yes	No
	1	2

In this example, only two choices are needed – you have either been skiing or you have not. If necessary, further categories can be used, such as a 'do not know' option.

When designing a questionnaire you are trying to make it as easy as possible to fill in, but also easy for you to report the results accurately and clearly. You should try and avoid **leading questions**, that is, ones where you are suggesting the answer in the question. 'Do you think football players receive too much money?' could be considered a leading question, as it almost implies that footballers are paid too much money. Also to be avoided are unclear terms. If a question begins with 'usually' or 'mostly', how often would you take this to mean? Once a day, once a week, or may be something different? Similarly, try not to use jargon or technical terms. If you ask a member of the public, 'How many times per week do you take part in aerobic exercise?' they may not understand the term aerobic. They may not answer the question or may answer it incorrectly. Not only do the questions need to be made very clear, but how you want them answered. Will there be tick boxes or do respondents circle a number.

Once you have compiled your questionnaire you should examine its usefulness. Try it out on a small group of people first (not the ones you aim to use it on later). Ask yourself some simple questions. Could it cause offence? Check the wording of the questions. Are all alternatives considered? If you ask 'Which sports do you enjoy?' and then proceed to give a list, what if somebody wants to put a sport you have not listed? You could include 'other' in the list or ask 'Which of the following sports do you enjoy?'. Is the response easy? People tend to fill in questionnaires as quickly as they can; they do not want to spend time having to complete the answers. Are there any overlapping categories? Asking how old somebody is and then having answers of 16–20, 20–24, for example, is annoying to a 20 year old. Which category are they in?

STUDENT ACTIVITY

Questionnaire design

1. Design a questionnaire to investigate an area of sport/exercise (e.g. exercise participation).
2. Use the questionnaire to obtain data.
3. Write a report of the results of the questionnaire and provide a brief discussion of these results.
4. Prepare a presentation of the results of your investigation (this can be done individually or as a group). Things to discuss in your presentation are:
   a) an explanation of the questionnaire (why you have asked certain questions, why they are in that order)
   b) the scoring/coding system; present the data in the most effective format (tables, graphs, etc.)
   c) an analysis of your results with constructive criticism (e.g. whether they could be improved, whether they are valid and reliable), and remember to have some implications at the end (what you have found, if you have any recommendations).

Interviews and observations

Questionnaires are used to collect general information from relatively large groups of people. With smaller groups (or with individuals) it is possible to gain more detailed information via an interview. Interviews are a method of information gathering used almost exclusively with qualitative research. An interview is normally a series of open-ended questions asked by the interviewer to the interviewee, and takes place face to face. To aid the interviewer the questions will be written down in advance. Supplementary questions can be asked if needed.

Information is usually recorded via a tape recorder or videotape. A tape recorder is less obtrusive (some people feel nervous faced with a video camera); however, the use of a videotape can give some non-verbal information that may prove beneficial. If a tape recorder or video camera is not available, the interviewer will have to record responses by hand. To become a good interviewer requires both ability and practice. If the answers obtained are to be valid it is essential that the respondent is relaxed and at ease. It is vital that the answers given are genuine and, for this reason, it is important that the interviewer does not influence the response by the nature of their questioning or even by their presence. As with questionnaires, the researcher is relying on what the subject says, which may or may not be the truth. Comparable techniques, as used with questionnaires, can be used to test the validity of a person's answer (i.e. repeated or similar questions can be asked to see if the answers are the same).

STUDENT ACTIVITY

Interview

1. Write a list of approximately 20 questions that you would like to ask a sports person of your choice.
2. Take part in a role play exercise where a fellow student pretends to be your chosen sports person. Conduct the interview using whichever method you wish to record the answers to your questions.
3. Write an evaluation of the interview stating what went well and how it could have been improved.

A further means of gaining information or data for research is to observe the subject in a given situation. Observations are common in psychology-based research – seeing what a person will do in a certain situation. This method is used because it is less obtrusive then administering a questionnaire or asking questions in an interview. Coaching is another area that relies on observations for obtaining information. In some sports, elaborate systems have been developed to code categories of actions or behaviour. These systems can be used by researchers to analyse coach or player behaviour, in addition to being used by the coach themselves to help players improve performance. A good example of this is in football, where notational analysis systems designed to examine the amount of activity (walking, running, jumping, etc.) undertaken by players of different positions can be used to devise individualised training programmes for players.

Sampling

In sport and exercise, when we take measurements for research purposes we are doing so for a group of people. If it were possible we would measure the entire population. The **population** is the whole group a researcher is interested in; the people the researcher wishes to draw conclusions about. If you measure the entire population and calculate a value like the average height, this is called a **parameter**. However, especially with large populations, it is more practical to examine a sample of the population (a smaller group). A value (the average height for example) which is based on a sample of a population is referred to as a **statistic**.

One method of selecting a sample is random sampling. **Random sampling** is a sampling technique where a group of subjects (a sample) is selected for study from a larger group (a population) by chance and all individuals have an equal chance of being included in the sample. With the use of random sampling, the chance of bias is reduced.

Bias refers to how far a statistic lies from the parameter it is estimating, that is, the error which occurs when estimating a value from a sample of a population. In other words, the value you obtain from a sample tends to be incorrect. The difference between the actual value (the parameter) and what you measure (the statistic) is called the **standard error**. The bigger your sample size, the less the standard error will be. This is because the greater your sample, the closer you are getting to measuring the whole population.

Numbers and units

When trying to measure the value or quantity of something, it is necessary to have a standard against which to compare. A unit is a standard by which a measured value can be described. There are two different sets of units used in measurements: British Engineering units (the imperial system) and the metric or SI system (*le Systéme International*). Most countries use the metric system (see Table 9.1), including Britain. In the United States, the British system is often used (for example, in boxing the Americans refer to a fight's weight (mass) in pounds (lbs)). However, for consistency in sport and exercise science research, the metric system is used.

Table 9.1 The SI system of measurement

Variable	Unit	Symbol
mass	kilograms	kg
length	metres	m
volume	litres	l
time	seconds	s
electric current	ampere	A
temperature	kelvin	K

Table 9.2 Common prefixes

Prefix	Symbol	Factor
giga	G	10^9
mega	M	10^6
kilo	k	10^3
centi	c	10^{-2}
milli	m	10^{-3}

The fundamental units are not always convenient (i.e. expressing the mass of a golf ball in kilograms is ridiculous), so prefixes are used to change the size of the unit (see Table 9.2). For example, 1000 metres (or 10^3 m) can be expressed as 1 km (kilometre).

Another important factor in recording a measurement, besides the unit, is the number of significant figures in the value. Significant figures should not be confused with decimal places. For example, 9.87 seconds is recorded to two decimal places, but has three significant figures. When using significant figures in calculations, the number of significant figures in the result should be the same as the number in the least precise measurement. For example: $4.28 \times 8.3 = 35.524$ before correction; after correction of significant figures, the result should be 36, since the limiting term (8.3) has only two significant figures.

Recording and displaying data

For numeric variables, one way to summarise the values is to graph them as a frequency distribution. One type of frequency distribution is a scatter plot, which shows a point for the number of times each value occurs. However, it is more common to show the frequencies as vertical bars rather than points, in which case the figure is called a histogram (see Figure 9.2). The most important consideration when displaying data is the presentation. The data should be summarised and displayed in the most effect format (there is no need to include all the raw data). Tables of data should include units and must have an appropriate title (which, by convention, is always placed above the table). Graphs should also include units and labels and have a title. Any picture, photograph or diagram including graphs and histograms but not tables, is referred to as a figure.

FIGURE 9.2 A histogram for age for a group of individuals

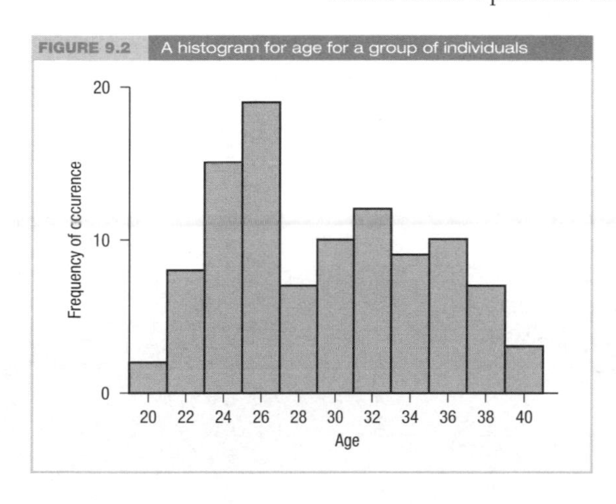

Displaying data

This activity should enable you to enter data into tables and to produce graphs. Based on the data in the table below, create tables with the following columns (in a spreadsheet, e.g. Excel or SPSS).

For male subjects:

Subject no | Height | Body mass | BMI | Endomorph | Mesomorph | Ectomorph

For female subjects:

Subject no | Height | Body Mass | BMI | Endomorph | Mesomorph | Ectomorph

- The data should be to one decimal place (e.g. 84.0).
- The last row in each table should contain an average of each column.
- The headings and averages should stand out clearly.
- Each table should be given a title to be placed above the table, e.g. Table 1. Anthropometric data for male subjects.

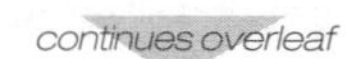
continues overleaf

Using the graph/chart option in a spreadsheet, produce a pie chart(s) to show average somatotype values (endomorph, mesomorph and ectomorph) for male and female subjects. The chart(s) should contain a title, actual values and descriptive labels. e.g. Figure 1. A comparison of average somatotypes for males and females.

Gender	Height (cm)	Mass (kg)	BMI	Endomorphy	Mesomorphy	Ectomorphy
M	186	80	23.4	2	4	3
M	187	74	21.2	1.5	2	4
M	190	82	22.7	2	4.5	3
M	177	72	23.0	2	4	4.5
M	188	78	22.1	3.5	3	2.5
M	176	97	31.3	5.5	8.5	0.5
M	185	89	26.0	3.5	5.5	2
M	179	66	20.6	1	4.5	4
M	192	84	22.7	3.5	3.5	3.5
M	190	85	23.5	4	5	3.5
F	165	55	20.8	3.5	2.5	3.5
F	163	75	20.2	4	3	1
F	165	51	19.0	2.5	3.5	4
F	168	51	18.7	1.5	2.5	4.5
F	156	57	23.4	4	2.5	1

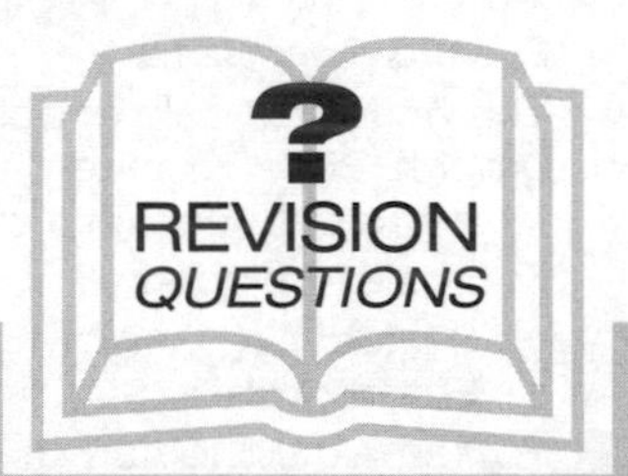

1) Explain what informed consent is.
2) Write an example of an informed consent form.
3) How does the Data Protection Act relate to research methods?
4) What are null, alternative and directional hypotheses?
5) Give an example of each type of hypothesis.
6) Explain what the benefits are of carrying out research using questionnaires.
7) What are the drawbacks with research that uses interviews to gain data?

INTERPRETING RESULTS

With a group of data, rather than displaying all the data, it is possible to use one number to represent all the data. This number is the average or central tendency. The three most commonly used measures of central tendency are the following.

1. **The mean**, which this is the sum of the values divided by the number of values. This is the most common type of average. For example, the mean of the following numbers: 8, 12, 16 and 24, would be calculated as follows:

$$\frac{8 + 12 + 16 + 24}{4} = 15.$$

2. **The median** is the value which divides the values into two equal halves, with half of the values being lower than the median and half higher than the median. If there are an odd number of values, the median is the middle value. With an even number of values, the median is the arithmetic mean (see above) of the two middle values. The median of the following five numbers: 23, 47, 50, 67 and 88, is 50.
3. **The mode** is the most frequently occurring value (or values) in the set. For individuals having the following ages, 17, 18, 19, 20, 20, 20, 23 and 27, the mode is 20.

For nominal data (such as gender), the mode is the only valid measure of central tendency. For ordinal data (such as league position), only the mode and median can be used.

STUDENT ACTIVITY

Central tendency

Choose an easily measurable variable, such as shoe size or height, then ask each member of your class to find out what the following class values are for your chosen variable:

mean
mode
median.

Dispersion

Some statistics give an idea of spread, variation or dispersion of the numbers. When a researcher talks about spread in a set of numbers, they may be referring to the difference in the scores (e.g. weight) across the group. Equally, the set of numbers could represent the weight of a single subject measured many times. The terms 'between-subject variation' and 'within-subject variation' are used to distinguish between these two types of spread. The simplest measure of spread is the **range**, expressed either as the biggest and smallest number in the data (e.g. 67–74), or as the difference between the biggest and smallest (e.g. 7). The range is a bad measure of spread because it is dependent on the size of your sample: the more numbers, the bigger the range is likely to be. It is also affected by outliers (see below). Two measures of spread that avoid these problems are the **standard deviation** (SD) and **percentile ranges**. Standard deviation is a measure of dispersion describing the spread of scores around the mean. The mean and standard deviation are often written as mean ± SD (e.g. 77.2 ± 1.8 kg). It has a complicated definition: take the distance of each number from the mean, square it, average the result, then take the square root. In short, it is the root mean square of the distances (or differences) from mean. The best way to think about the standard deviation is that about two-thirds of the values of a variable are found within one deviation each side of the mean (for normally distributed data, see below). Inter-quartile range is similar to range, but it discounts the top and bottom 25% of the data. The type of dispersion used depends on the measure of central tendency. With mean, the standard deviation is normally used. For the median it is the inter-quartile range, and with the mode it is range.

Central tendency and dispersion

1 For the following set of data, calculate or determine the mean, median and mode (this can be done easily in a spreadsheet).
2 Comment on why the values are different. It may help to plot a frequency distribution (histogram).
3 In addition, calculate or determine the standard deviation, inter-quartile range and range (use a spreadsheet).

Subject	1	2	3	4	5	6	7	8	9	10	11
Age	22	19	16	21	23	27	24	19	26	19	17

Normal distribution

Normally distributed data looks like that in Figure 9.3, that is, it peaks in the middle. In this example, if we measured IQ for a sample of the population we could say that the majority of people have an average IQ, while a small number have high and low values.

Normally distributed data is typically bell-shaped when graphed (see Figure 9.3). The distribution is theoretical because the height of the curve is defined by a mathematical formula. In a true normal distribution, the mean, median and mode are all the same value. If the distribution is asymmetrical the data is not normally distributed, which can be due to skewness (the peak is more to the left or right) or kurtosis (the curve excessively peaked or flat). A **negative skew** is asymmetry in a distribution in which the scores are bunched to the right side of the centre, while a **positive skew** is asymmetry in a distribution in which the scores are bunched to the left side of the centre. A **latykurtic curve** is when the distribution is flatter than a normal distribution. This is to say that there are more cases in the extremes of the distribution than would normally be the case. The opposite of this is **leptokurtic**: this is when a distribution is more peaked than a normal distribution; there are more cases concentrated close to the mean than in a normal distribution. Whether or not the data is normally distributed determines which measure of central tendency and dispersion to select. The other information that is needed is the level of measurement (i.e. interval, ratio, nominal – see Table 9.3).

FIGURE 9.3 Data displaying normal distribution

Table 9.3 Which measure of central tendency to select based on the distribution of the data and the level of measurement.

Central tendency	Data
Mean	interval/ratio data and normally distributed
Median	data that is not normally distributed (e.g. skewed)
Mode	nominal data and normally distributed

There is a general rule that applies with a normal or bell-shaped distribution. Starting with the average (the centre of the distribution), if you go left and right one standard deviation, you will include approximately 65% of the cases in the distribution. If you go left and right two standard deviations, you will include approximately 95% of the cases. If you go plus or minus three standard deviations, you will include 99% of the cases.

Outliers

Outliers are unusual data values. They can occur due to data recording or entry errors. Alternatively, they may be caused by some rare event or extreme observation (such as a thermometer left in direct sunlight, or a subject who has an abrupt change in heart rate). The problem with outliers is that some statistics (e.g. the mean) can be distorted, which can lead to faulty conclusions. In such cases the median would be a more dependable measure of central tendency, as it is not affected greatly by outliers. There is a temptation to ignore outliers, but only as a final option should you delete them. This could be done if you find there are genuine errors (results that should not have been recorded) that cannot be corrected. If you have any uncertainty, you can include results both with and without outliers to see how much they differ.

STUDENT PRACTICAL

Normal distribution

Aim

The aims of this activity are to determine if data is normally distributed and to produce an appropriate measure of central tendency.

Method

1 Enter the data from the table into a spreadsheet (e.g. Excel or SPSS), coding where appropriate.
2 Produce a variable to illustrate the difference between resting heart rate and maximum heart rate.
3 Sort your data by the age variable (descending order).
4 For each variable, look at the data and determine the level of measurement (e.g. nominal, ordinal, interval/ratio).

continues overleaf

continued

5 For variables that are at the interval/ratio level, determine whether they are normally distributed. To do this you will need to produce a histogram: if you are using Excel you will have to make a new table from which you can create the histogram; in SPSS you can just select 'histogram'. From this information you can establish the appropriate measure of central tendency and dispersion for each variable.

Age	Sport	Heart rate (rest)	Heart rate (max)
18	Badminton	80	200
19	Football	81	180
19	Hockey	88	182
18	Climbing	72	200
20	Hockey	66	189
29	Football	77	175
25	Hockey	72	200
19	Hockey	69	176
18	Football	72	190
19	Hockey	69	191
19	Hockey	79	192
19	Hockey	62	188
18	Hockey	62	193
19	Football	79	189
19	Badminton	63	193
19	Climbing	87	183
20	Climbing	68	194
19	Golf	49	183
19	Climbing	76	198
20	Badminton	57	194

Statistical tests

Numerical analysis of data is called statistics. **Descriptive statistics** are just that, describing data (i.e. central tendency and dispersion). **Inferential statistics** are more in depth – rather than just describing data they examine relationships and differences in data. They can be used to determine the answer to your research question or your hypothesis. Inferential statistics analyse whether the null hypothesis is true or false (at a given level of significance). Relationships look at how one thing affects another and are analysed via correlations. Differences determine if one group (or set of data) is different from another. There are numerous difference tests that will be explained letter.

Correlations

To measure if two things are related, a correlation can be performed. Correlation means association or relationship. For example, if the question 'Is heart rate related to environmental temperature?' is asked, it can be answered with a test of correlation. The correlation will give an exact quantification of the association between the two factors. This value or number is called the **correlation coefficient** and is commonly symbolised by the letter **r**. If two variables are in perfect association, so that as one increases so does the other (without exception), they have a **perfect positive correlation**. The correlation coefficient (r) to represent this is +1. If there is absolutely no relationship r is 0. However, if the association is inverse, where one goes up as the other goes down, this is described as a **negative correlation**. For this, r is denoted by –1. Thus, r can be any value between +1 and –1 (see Figure 9.4).

FIGURE 9.4 Correlation coefficients

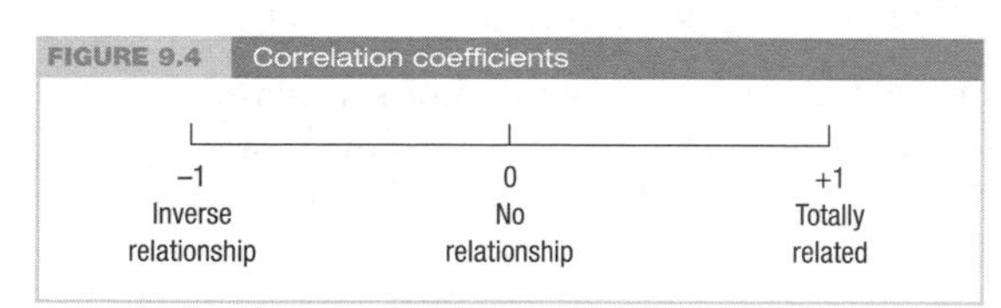

FIGURE 9.5 Scatterplot showing a positive correlation

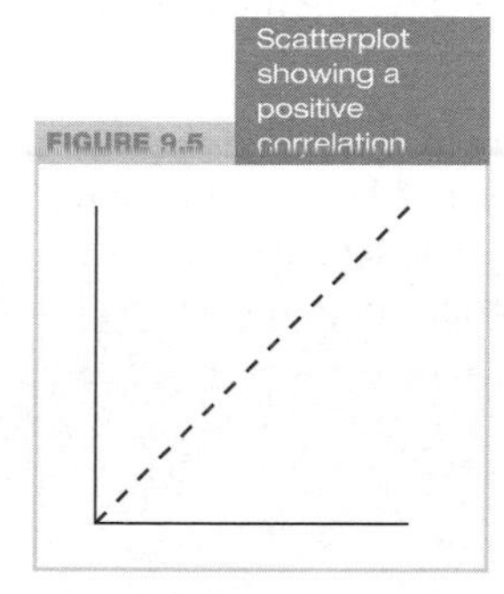

Visually, the correlation or association can be displayed by a scattergram or scatterplot, as shown in Figure 9.5.

It must be remembered that a high correlation, association or relationship is just that; it does not necessarily mean that one variable causes the other. Association does not mean causation.

Having measured r, how can it be interpreted? What does it mean? When a correlation is performed, besides an r value being reported, a probability or **significance value** is given. This significance value is given as a decimal (e.g. 0.10). This value indicates the probability of what you are testing being true or untrue. For example, if you were testing a relationship, a significance value of 0.10 would mean that 10 times in 100 you would be wrong if you said there was a relationship (it could be due to luck). Which means 90 times in 100 you would be correct. In social science (e.g. sports science, psychology, etc.) the accepted significance value is 0.05 (being wrong 5 times in 100). If the significance value is higher than 0.05 then there is no relationship (or at least, it is not significant). Statistically, the specific significance value of 0.05 is written as $p < .05$, which means the probability must be less than 5 in 100.

A further measure that can be calculated is the **coefficient of determination**. This indicates the amount of influence one variable has over another. The coefficient of determination is equal to r^2 and is often given as a percentage (e.g. .50 is 50%). For a correlation of .70 (r), the coefficient of determination would be .49 (r^2), which means 49% of the variance in a factor is due to the other variable – obviously 51% is due to other things. Returning to the question, 'Is heart rate related to environmental temperature?', a coefficient of determination of 0.49 would suggest that 49% of the variance (change) in heart rate is due to changes in environmental temperature, and 51% of the variance is due to other factors.

Pearson product-moment correlation

A Pearson product-moment correlation is one type of test that can be performed. In order to do this, a number of criteria must be met. The underlying assumptions are as follows.

- **Data** must be from **related pairs**, i.e. it should be collected from the same subject (e.g. height and mass from the same person)
- **Data** should be **interval or ratio** (explained previously).
- Each variable should be normally distributed (**normality**). There are a number of ways to explore this e.g. skewness and kurtosis

- The relationship of the two variables must be linear (**linearity**). Linearity is assessed using a scatter plot, and is determined from the shape of the data: if it forms a straight line (roughly), it is said to be linear.
- Variability in scores should be roughly the same (**homoscedascity**). Homoscedascity is also assessed using a scatter plot. If the scores cluster uniformly around a straight line through the points, then homoscedascity can be assumed.

If the assumptions for a Pearson product-moment correlation are not met then a Spearman rank-order correlation is performed.

If the relationship is significant, the statistics would be reported as ($r = .844$, $p < .05$). The Pearson product-moment correlation r value is .844. That is a strong positive relationship between the two variables measured. The significance value is less than .05; this means the relationship is statistically significant (it is meaningful).

Correlation

An exercise physiologist is interested to see if there is a relationship between maximum volume of oxygen consumed (maxVO_2) as measured in a physiology lab and marathon performance (best time to run a marathon). The results collected are given below.

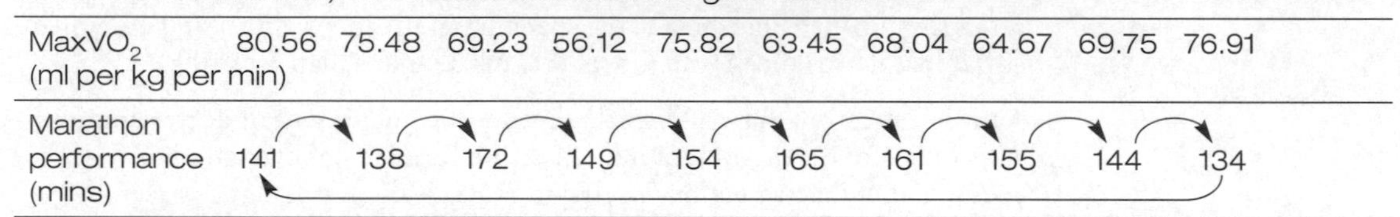

MaxVO_2 (ml per kg per min)	80.56	75.48	69.23	56.12	75.82	63.45	68.04	64.67	69.75	76.91
Marathon performance (mins)	141	138	172	149	154	165	161	155	144	134

1. Identify the null and alternative hypotheses for this inquiry.
2. Determine which test of correlation is appropriate and run the test in EXCEL, SPSS or a similar spreadsheet.
3. From your results explain the value of the correlation coefficient and what it means.
4. Which hypothesis should be accepted and why?
5. What might affect the results?

Difference tests

Difference tests can be divided into two types: parametric and non-parametric statistics. **Parametric** statistics are used when the data is normally distributed and interval/ratio level. **Non-parametric** statistics are often referred to as distribution-free statistics, as they are used when the data may not demonstrate the characteristics of normality (i.e. follow a normal distribution). They are used with nominal data, where the response set can be converted to counts of events, and the measurement scale is ignored. As in all research designs, there are specific assumptions which underlie the selection of the various statistical procedures.

Difference tests are evaluative procedures for studying the effect of a given treatment on a randomly selected group of individuals, for example, how training affects fitness levels. Following the imposition of the experimental condition (treatment), the researcher tests whether the experimental condition was effective by observing the distributions of the responses on a selected dependent measure (fitness). The results of difference tests are reported in a similar way to correlations, but instead of referring to a significant relationship, a significant difference is talked about. For example, there is a significant difference ($t = 1.352$, $p < .05$) in heart rate between a group that does exercise and a group that does not.

With parametric data the most common difference tests are t-tests. An **independent t-test** is used when investigating differences between groups (the samples are independent, hence the name). The **dependent t-test** is used when the data is from the same group (paired samples) and you are examining a difference within the group.

If the data is not parametric, then t-tests can not be performed, so alternative tests must be used. The Mann-Whitney U test is a non-parametric difference test that can be used with different groups (independent samples). The Wilcoxon matched-pairs test is a non-parametric test that can be used with paired samples (data from one group).

The Chi square test is a further non-parametric test that is used to compare observed frequency in a group with expected group frequency (the frequency due to a chance occurrence). It requires nominal data from independent categories with a large sample size.

t-test

A fitness instructor runs two different circuit training classes. She thinks that one class may more strenuous than the other. She measures the heart rates of the members of each of the two classes (no one attends both classes). The average heart rate for each person during the session is given below (values are in bpm).

Class 1	123	132	117	143	129	136	118	134	111	127	124	115	128	130	122	112
Class 2	136	128	136	131	115	117	151	147	126	135	128	134	116	129	136	127

1 Identify the null and alternative hypotheses for this inquiry.
2 Determine which t-test is appropriate and run the test in Excel, SPSS or a similar spreadsheet package.
3 From your results, explain what the significance value means.
4 Which hypothesis should be accepted and why?
5 What might affect the results?

1) Distinguish between the mean, median and mode.
2) How do you explain the different types of central tendency?
3) Explain the concept of dispersion.
4) What is a correlation and how is it determined?
5) What are the different measures of correlation?

1) Explain the following terms: reliability, validity and objectivity.
2) What are the ethical issues involved in research in sport?
3) How would you go about designing a questionnaire?
4) What is normally distributed data?
5) Outline the use of a variety of statistical tests.

SUGGESTED FURTHER READING

Clegg, F. (1993) *Simple Statistics: A Course Book for the Social Sciences*. Cambridge University Press

Silverman, D. (2001) *Doing Qualitative Research: A Practical Guide*. Sage Publications

Thomas, J. R. and Nelson, J. K. (2001) *Research Methods in Physical Activity*. 4th Edition. Illinois: Human Kinetics

TEN STEPS TO A GREAT IVA

What is the IVA?

IVA stands for **Integrated Vocational Assignment**. This is a specific piece of work you will do for your BTEC National qualification.

The IVA is set by Edexcel, marked by your tutors and the assessment is checked by Edexcel. The IVA is **compulsory**. You cannot gain the complete award unless you attempt it. Obviously, though, you should do a lot more than just attempt it! Indeed, it is sensible to aim as high as you can. You might even surprise yourself.

This guide gives you hints and tips on researching and completing your IVA so that you will target all your efforts productively. In other words, you won't waste time doing things that aren't needed or you weren't intended to do! This doesn't mean that you can get by without doing any work at all. It does mean that you will get the maximum benefit for the work that you do.

Step 1: Understanding the basics

The IVA is a set of tasks you have to do. The tasks only relate to one or two specific units. These are identified on the front cover of the IVA. You will only be expected to complete tasks after you have learned about the unit(s) in class.

The IVA *must* be all your own work. If you have to do part of the work as a member of a group then the conclusions you write must be your own. If any part of the work has been done with someone else this must be clearly stated. This also means that you should not share your ideas or your researched information with anyone or copy anyone else's work

The IVA is not an examination. It is a series of tasks that you have to do to check that you understand the information you have learned. If you can demonstrate that you can apply and use this information in more than one situation and make informed judgements then you will gain a higher grade. You will be expected to research your own information to add to the work you have done in class. However, you must always list and identify your sources and never try to pass them off as you own work. How to do this is shown under Step 4.

You can produce your IVA over a period of time. Your tutor will tell you how long you have to complete it when it is issued. Make sure you know your deadlines for each stage and for any reviews that you have with your tutor. These will be included on a **Centre IVA Issue Sheet** that your tutor will give you. It also includes information about the resources you can use and support that is available to you. Keep this sheet safely and enter all the dates into your diary or onto your wall planner immediately. It is also sensible to enter a 'warning' a week before each important date, to remind yourself that it is looming!

Always remember that if you have any worries or concerns about your IVA then you should talk to your tutor. Don't wait for the next review date to do this – especially if the problem is serious.

Help yourself . . .

. . . by making sure you possess a diary or wall planner on which you can write deadline dates when you receive your Centre IVA issue sheet.

Step 2: Obtaining your IVA

You are unlikely to be expected to start your IVA until you have completed most, if not all, of the unit(s) to which it relates. However, you might be given it sooner so that you know what to expect and you can see the actual tasks you will have to answer.

You can see the IVA at any time, yourself, by logging onto the Edexcel website at www.edexcel.org.uk . Click on to 'qualifications', then select 'BTEC National' then click on the subject you are studying. The document you want is entitled *IVA – Learner Instructions.* It is normally quite short, between 8 and 10 pages, and contains the following information.

- The title page, which gives you
  - the level and title of your BTEC National qualification
  - the subject
  - the unit(s) to which the IVA relates
  - the date of issue and specification to which it relates. Ask your tutor if you are not sure whether this matches your course.
- Full instructions for completing and presenting the IVA. This is on page 2. It is very important that you read this carefully.
- Your assignment tasks and a copy of the assessment criteria grid(s). You will find out more about these under Step 3.

Help yourself . . .

. . . by starting a special IVA file that includes the IVA, the Centre IVA issue sheet and any specific notes your tutor gives you relating to the IVA.

Step 3: Understanding the tasks

This is the most important step of all. If you don't understand what you have to do to answer a question then you are very unlikely to get a good grade. You may do a lot of work but much of it may be irrelevant or – more likely – you will miss out important information.

It is quite normal for students to panic when they first read a set of assignment tasks! For this reason you are likely to be introduced to your IVA in a special session held by your tutor. Although your tutor cannot do the work for you (obviously!) you are allowed to receive guidance and can discuss general ideas, just like you would for an internal assessment. Your tutor can also answer any queries you have and give you ongoing advice and support in your review sessions to help you to do your best.

All IVAs are written in a certain format, or design.

- They start with a scenario or context to 'set the scene'. This may be quite short – just a few lines – or take up most of a page.

- Below this are several tasks. Each task usually starts with some introductory or background information and is then divided into lettered sub-sections.
- You are often expected to provide your answer in a specific document, such as a report, a letter, a leaflet, a table or a summary.
- At the end of each task you will see the unit number and assessment criteria covered by that task, eg Unit 2, P1, M1, D1. In this case it would mean that particular task related to Unit 2 and your answer must focus on providing evidence against the first assessment criterion under each of the pass, merit and distinction columns. You can match up this information in the assessment criteria grid(s). Your tutor will show you how to do this if you are not sure.

You will not be expected to do all the tasks at once. Let's assume you have been told to start with Task 1. There are two things you can do to make sure you understand *exactly* what you have to do.

1 Break the task down into chunks and analyse it.

2 Complete a task checklist before you start work.

You will read how to do this in Steps 4 and 5.

Help yourself . . .

. . . by first reading all the tasks you will have to do to get the overall picture and then reading – far more carefully – the first task you have to do. Then note down anything that puzzles you or that you do not understand.

Step 4: Analyse the task

Although IVAs aren't meant to be daunting or difficult to understand, it can be useful to know what to do if you do experience any problems. If a scenario or a task is short it is normally easier to understand. If it is long it may be more difficult. This is because there is more 'additional' information and if you miss any of this, it may affect your grade.

If there is a lot of information don't expect to understand it fully the first time you read it. Just read it to get a general impression. Then read it again, more slowly, to get the meaning. It is often helpful to go through it again, much more thoroughly, to identify the important words. This is called **task analysis**. The aim is to identify:

- the **background information** – which sets the scene or the context. You need to understand this for the task to make sense
- the **command words**, such as 'describe' or 'explain' – which tell you what you have to do. You *must* obey these when you answer the questions. If you are unsure what any of these words mean, check back to the explanation in *The Smart Way to Achieve Your BTEC National* at the start of this book
- other **specific instructions** which tell you what you have to do – such as 'provide three examples' or 'write a report'
- any important **topic words** which give you the subject of the task.

Finally, make sure you now understand the purpose of the task you have to do and the audience you are preparing it for. Both these factors affect the way you will structure and present your answer.

Task 1: Prove your understanding of the IVA

Edexcel issues an assessment called an IVA that covers the whole of either one or two units of a BTEC National programme. This tests all learners nationally on the same set of tasks. Produce a short report which identifies your own tasks in relation to your IVA. Your report should include:

a A brief **description** of the IVA.

b An **explanation** of the main instructions given to learners. This must include the **identification** of three requirements which ensure that each IVA is the student's own original work.

c Your own plan for producing your IVA which shows how you have **analysed** your options and provides **justifications** for the decisions you have made.

Background information which sets the scene.

To produce a short report, and what the report should include are both instructions. Your own tasks in relation to the IVA are topic words

'Brief' is an instruction, 'of the IVA' is the topic. 'Description' and 'explanation' are both **command words**. 'Must include' is an instruction but 'identification' is a command word. The remaining words are topic words except for 'three' which is an instruction.

'Your own plan' is an instruction. The remaining words give you the topic. This must involve 'analysis' and 'justification', so these are both **command words**.

Help yourself . . .

. . . by practising task analysis yourself.

In agreement with your tutor, select **one** task in the IVA you have been issued and carry out the following tasks.

a Identify the background information, command words, instructions and topic words that it contains. You can use any combination of colour or highlighting (such as bold or underscore) that you find easiest to understand.

b Explain the purpose of that task and identify your audience. Then say how these two factors will influence your answer.

c Compare your ideas with those of other members of your group.

Step 5: Completing a task checklist

This will confirm if you really do understand what you have to do. Simply read the following list. If you can complete the column on the right with ticks then you understand the task. If you can't then you must resolve the problem before you start work.

Checklist for understanding your IVA task		✓ or x
Read the scenario or context that 'sets the scene'	Does it make sense? Do you understand all the words used? Can you identify the key words? Would it help you to highlight these? Could you accurately explain the scenario or context to someone else, using your own words?	
Read the task you have to do and then analyse it	Have you carried out task analysis? Can you identify the background information? Can you identify *all* the command words? Can you identify *all* the instructions? Do you understand the topics? Can you clearly state what you have to do, using your own words? Do you know how to set out the document(s) you have to produce?	
Do you know the purpose of the task and have you identified your audience?	Can you explain the reason for doing this task? Who is your audience? How will these two factors affect your answer?	
Check the evidence statement at the bottom of the task and check this against the assessment criteria grid	Do you know the grades you can get for this task? Can you see how the command words differ within the task to cover merit and distinction questions? Are you *certain* that you know what is meant by each command word?	

- If you don't understand a word that is used then look in a dictionary or check the list of command words and their meanings given in *The Smart Way to Achieve your BTEC National.*
- If there is any instruction that you do not understand, such as how to set out a document that is required, talk to your tutor.
- If there is any aspect of the topic that you missed when it was covered in class then talk to your tutor about obtaining the information you need.

Help yourself . . .

. . . copy the checklist and complete it for the first task on your list. Remember that you *must* obtain help if you still cannot understand anything about the task you have to do.

Step 6: Planning your work

Completing any task(s) will take some time. You have to allow enough time for obtaining the information, deciding what to use, getting it into the right order and writing it up. You also need to bear in mind the review date(s) agreed with your tutor – as well as all the other college and personal commitments you have! It is therefore sensible to make a plan.

- The IVA is designed to cover the unit content and each task covers different parts of the unit. You can check which parts of a unit are covered by a particular task by looking at the key words. These will relate to the assessment criteria for the unit and the unit specification, which gives detailed information on the content.

- Next estimate how long it will take you to find the information you need. You will do this more accurately if you identify your information sources. Although this will obviously depend on the format of your IVA and the task you are doing you will probably want to refer to

  - notes you have been given in class
  - your course textbook
  - two or three library books or journals
  - some online resources.

  If you are researching for a project or need to use evidence from a particular event then you may need to arrange to talk to people to get their views. You must therefore allow enough time to obtain your information.
- Decide how long it is likely to take to sort through your information before you can start to write your first draft answer.
- Allow time for rereading and revising your answer and then for checking the way you have presented the information.
- Decide how many hours a week you will need to spend on your IVA to stay on schedule.
- Split these up into sensible sessions. Longer than two or three hours is too much – you won't work well when you're tired. Shorter than half an hour isn't much good unless you've a specific small job to do.
- Identify times during the week when you will do the work and mark these in your diary or on your wall planner, eg Tuesday 5 pm – 7 pm. Then stick to them! If an emergency means you can't work at that time remember that you then need to reschedule these hours at another time to keep on target!

Help yourself . . .

. . . by always allowing more time than you think you will need, never less. You should also find a quiet place to work, where you can concentrate. Now make out your plan for the first task you have to do. Aim to finish a week early to allow time for slippage.

Step 7: Researching, storing and selecting your information

Problems with researching are always linked to the quality and quantity of information. For information to be good quality it needs to relate directly to the topic. You also need to understand it! Quantity is also important. If you only rely on your course notes then you are unlikely to produce original work and this will affect your grade, but too much information is very confusing and you are likely to get bogged down trying to decide what to use.

Start by listing all the potential sources of information you can use. These will depend largely upon the type of task you are doing and the information you need.

- If you are looking for books you are best to aim for two or three that specifically cover the topic. Check this by looking in the index when you are in the library, then skim the text to make sure it is written at the right level and that you find the style 'user-friendly'. You are wise to schedule in a prompt visit to your college library – particularly if there are many students doing the same IVA as you!
- If you are searching online you will have far more success if you learn how to do advanced searches on websites such as Google. It is also important to keep focused and not get distracted by interesting but irrelevant information you come across as you search! If you need help searching on line, talk to the IT resource staff at college.
- If you need to visit organisations or interview someone then prepare well in advance. Make the arrangement and then draft a list of questions. If you want to take a tape recorder, first check this is acceptable.

- If you are preparing a presentation that involves other people in your group arrange a first meeting to decide your roles and responsibilities. Check in your library for useful guidelines on preparing and giving a presentation.
- Buy a box file and label it. If you are broke use an empty cardboard box! Put in every scrap of information that might be helpful for your IVA. If your IVA covers two units then you might find it helpful to keep the information that relates to each one in separate folders.
- Make sure that all the information you put into your box file is dated and labelled with its source (see below). This includes any photocopies you have taken or print-outs you have made.
- Have a cut-off date when you stop collecting information and start to write. If you don't, you can easily find yourself running out of time to complete the task.
- Only select the most relevant information after re-reading the task *and* your task analysis. It's often easiest to start by spreading out all your information on a large table (or the floor!). Then select everything you think you might need and put the rest away.
- Read through your information and make draft notes to answer the question. *Don't* copy out reams of information – note down the source of the information instead. Remember that most of your IVA must be in your own words.
- Make sure you only include relevant information and that you re-word or adapt information to match the task you are doing. It is very tempting to 'cut and paste' lots of information, particularly from the Internet, just because you found it! A good trick is to keep looking back to the question at regular intervals to keep yourself focused and *never* include everything 'just 'cos it's there'! Remember that marks are always awarded for quality of work, not quantity!

Help yourself . . .

. . . by being self-disciplined when you are looking for information. This means not getting distracted, *always* noting down the source of information you print out or photocopy and *always* storing it safely so you can find it again!

Step 8: Identifying your sources

You must do this if you quote from any source. If you forget then you could be guilty of plagiarism. This is a serious academic crime as it is assumed that you were trying to pass off someone else's work as your own. It is so serious that some colleges and universities have installed special software to catch plagiarists!

Your tutor or your college library will be able to give you detailed information on citing references. If not, use the following as your guide.

In the text:

- Always put quoted information in quotation marks. Mark Twain said 'There are lies, damned lies and statistics.'
- If you refer to an author put their name and then the date and/or page number in brackets. Chaffey (2002) argues that . . . .

At the end of the task, in your bibliography, list your references in alphabetical order of author. Put the title in bold or in italics so that it stands out.

- If your source is a newspaper or magazine, state the name of the author(s), year of publication in brackets, title of the article, the title of the publication, volume or date, pages of the article eg Gascoigne, C (2005) **Leading from the front**, Sunday Times Smarter Business, 6 February 2005, page 7.
- If your source is a book, give the author(s), date of publication in brackets, title and the publisher eg Chaffey, D (2002) **E-Business and E-Commerce Management**, Prentice Hall, page 25.

- If your source is from the Internet then you should give enough information for your tutor to be able to find the article online. However, you are also wise to keep your print-out as Internet sites are regularly updated and you may need proof of your information. It is recommended that you give the name of the person or organisation responsible for the article or site, the title of the document, the word Internet in square brackets, the URL and the date you accessed the information. This is the address line that shows on screen and is normally printed at the bottom of the page eg Sport England, **What the 2012 Olympics would do for the UK**, [Internet], http://www.sportengland.org/index/news_and_media/olympics_2012/2012_uk.htm [Accessed 7 February 2005]

Help yourself . . .

. . . by checking if there is a course or college guide to citing references. Ask your tutor or librarian if you are not sure. Alternatively you can test your research skills by finding information online. Type 'Harvard referencing' into any search engine. This is the most usual method used by students at university.

Step 9: Writing and presenting your IVA

The first thing to do is to plan your answer. Re-read your task analysis to refresh your memory. Check carefully the command words, the instructions and the topic words. Make sure you know what type of document you have to produce and how to set it out.

There are two ways in which you can plan your answer. Use the one that is most natural for you:

1 Write a list of all the information you want to include. Then put it into the correct order. Decide what will go in the introduction, what in the middle of the answer and what your conclusion will be.

2 Write the question in the middle of the page and write your information around it. Link the information with arrows so you end up with different themes. Decide the best order to introduce each theme and how these will be reflected in your paragraphs.

If you find that you are missing any information write this on a 'to do' list. You can still plan and draft your answer. Your 'to do' list is to make certain you don't forget to find out the remaining details.

Decide the approach you want to use. For example, if you have to contrast and compare two things then you could write all about one and then the other; alternatively you could describe each one and then analyse the similarities and differences afterwards. *Neither is right or wrong* – do the one you find easier. If you find that it then doesn't work very well when you start to draft your answer, be prepared to change it.

Don't think that you need to write in a more flowery or grandiose style than you normally do. In fact, there are lots of pitfalls if you do this – such as using the wrong word or writing a complex sentence that no-one can understand! Instead, keep your writing style simple and only use words you understand. If you also keep your sentences relatively short but vary the length a little then your answer will also be more interesting and easier to read.

Don't expect to write the answers to merit and distinction level questions quickly. These are deliberately written to make you think! Look back at the command words information and examples in *The Smart Way to Achieve your BTEC National* if you are struggling. Then draft your answer as best you can and discuss your ideas with your tutor at your next review meeting. This might help to put you on the right track again.

The type of task and your audience will determine your writing style. If you are asked to prepare a formal business document such as a report it is better to use a quite formal writing style. In this case try to write using the third person. This means you don't say 'I think that ' but 'it is considered that' or 'it would appear that'. Equally you wouldn't say 'You can do this by . . .' but 'This could be done by . . . '. The situation is different, though, if you are preparing an informal account, such as an article for a staff newsletter. In every document, though, you should avoid using slang or contracted words (eg can't or hasn't) and *never* use the abbreviated words or jargon that you would use in a text message or if you were talking to your friends.

Leave your work alone for a day or two before you make a final check. This way you are more likely to spot errors. You may also find this easier to do if you take a print-out rather than read it on screen. Check it against the question. Have you obeyed all the command words? Have you included everything that was asked for? Is the information given in a logical order?

Now check the presentation and your writing style. Have you set out the document correctly? Is it in the right style? For example a letter or report must be set out in the right format and not written as an essay style answer. Is the grammar correct? Is every word spelt properly? Don't rely on your spellchecker here. It cannot tell the difference between 'hear' and 'here' or 'there' and 'their'! Word processing packages are also very limited in their ability to correct grammatical errors, so never assume that you don't need to check your work carefully yourself. If you are preparing a draft print-out to discuss with your tutor it is useful to use wide margins and double spacing then you have plenty of room to note down comments.

Make sure you have included a sheet with all your references on it. It is usually easier to compile this as you go – rather than create these at the end when some notes will be buried under a mountain of paper.

Finally check that the presentation of your IVA matches *all* the requirements set out on page 2 of your *Instructions for Learners completing IVAs*. For example, you must not put your work into plastic pockets or into a box file or a lever arch file. You also need to put a cover sheet on the front and sign a declaration that all the work you are submitting is your own.

Help yourself . . .

. . . by asking someone you trust to read through your work and make comments. This can be a close friend or a family member but shouldn't be a fellow student who is doing the same IVA as you. If your friend or relative can't understand what you are trying to say then it is probably true that your tutor will have the same problem!

Step 10: Is this the best you can do?

It always seems a tragedy when students just miss a better grade because of carelessness or silly mistakes. As a final check, before you give in your work, run through the following list. Only hand in your work when, hand on heart, you know you honestly couldn't do any more.

- You have incorporated all the suggestions and ideas that you discussed with your tutor at your review meetings.
- You have answered every part of every task and there are no gaps or omissions.
- You have addressed all the command words correctly and taken account of all the instructions.
- You have checked the spelling, punctuation and layout.
- You have checked and double-checked that all the references are included.
- All your pages are numbered and your name is on every sheet.
- You have followed every other instruction for completing and presenting your work. Do a final check of page 2 of your *Instructions for Learners completing IVAs* before you hand in your work. For example, are all your pages in the right order and are they securely fastened together?

Help yourself . . .

. . . by handing in your work before the deadline and then relaxing! Once you have done your best and submitted your work you cannot then alter the grade for that particular piece of work. Remember, though, that the grade you achieve is very important feedback for future work you will do. Learn from your mistakes and build on your successes – and your work will always continue to improve.

BTEC National Study Guide

SPORT AND EXERCISE SCIENCES

The chapters in this Study Guide are all taken from

BTEC NATIONAL SPORT AND EXERCISE SCIENCE
by Jennifer Stafford-Brown, Simon Rea and John Chance, published by Hodder Arnold